**REGENTS PREPARATION, LLC.**

-Presents-

GEOMETRY
REGENTS EXAM
REVIEW MANUAL

WITH 9 REGENTS EXAMS,
7 TOPICALLY ORGANIZED

Production

Printed in the United States of America
ISBN: 978-0-578-19770-8

Geometry

Table of Contents

Angle and Segment Relationships

1 In the diagram below, lines ℓ, m, n, and p intersect line r.

08 2016 01

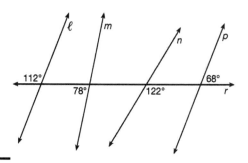

Which statement is true?

~~1)~~ $\ell \parallel n$ **2)** $\ell \parallel p$

~~3)~~ $m \parallel p$ ~~4)~~ $m \parallel n$

2. Segment *CD* is the perpendicular bisector of $\overline{AB}$ at *E*. Which pair of segments does *not* have to be congruent?

08 2016 11

1) $\overline{AD}, \overline{BD}$ **2)** $\overline{AC}, \overline{BC}$

3) $\overline{AE}, \overline{BE}$ 4) $\overline{DE}, \overline{CE}$

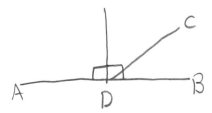

3. In the diagram below, $\overleftrightarrow{FE}$ bisects $\overline{AC}$ at B, and $\overleftrightarrow{GE}$ bisects $\overline{BD}$ at C.

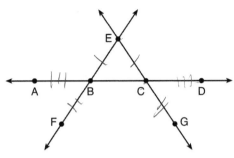

Which statement is always true?

1) $\overline{AB} \cong \overline{DC}$ ✓
2) $\overline{FB} \cong \overline{EB}$
3) $\overleftrightarrow{BD}$ bisects $\overline{GE}$ at C. ✓
4) $\overleftrightarrow{AC}$ bisects $\overline{FE}$ at B.

4. Steve drew line segments ABCD, EFG, BF, and CF as shown in the diagram below. Scalene $\triangle BFC$ is formed.

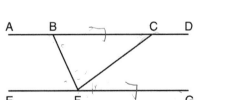

2

Which statement will allow Steve to prove $\overline{ABCD} \parallel \overline{EFG}$?

1) $\angle CFG \cong \angle FCB$ ✓
2) $\angle ABF \cong \angle BFC$
3) $\angle EFB \cong \angle CFB$
4) $\angle CBF \cong \angle GFC$

5. In the diagram below, $\overline{EF}$ intersects $\overline{AB}$ and $\overline{CD}$ at G and H, respectively, and $\overline{GI}$ is drawn such that $\overline{GH} \cong \overline{IH}$.

06 2015 32

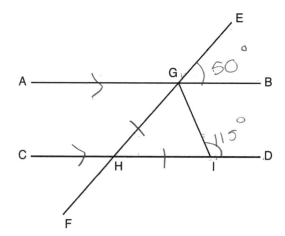

If m$\angle EGB = 50°$ and m$\angle DIG = 115°$, explain why $\overline{AB} \parallel \overline{CD}$.

They are // bc they are
Corresponding ∢'s

Angle and Segment Relationships in Triangles and Polygons

1. Keira has a square poster that she is framing and placing on her wall. The poster has a diagonal 58 cm long and fits exactly inside the frame. The width of the frame around the picture is 4 cm.

08 2017 34

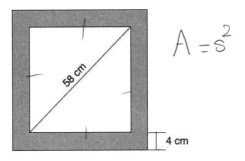

$A = s^2$

4 cm

Determine and state the total area of the poster and frame to the *nearest tenth of a square centimeter*.

2. Given $\triangle ABC$ with $m\angle B = 62°$ and side $\overline{AC}$ extended to D, as shown below.

08 2017 11

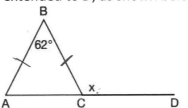

4

Which value of x makes $\overline{AB} \cong \overline{CB}$?

$180 - 62 = 118$

1) 59º

⓪ 118º

2) 62º

4) 121º

3. In the diagram below of triangle MNO, $\angle M$ and $\angle O$ are bisected by $\overline{MS}$ and $\overline{OR}$, respectively. Segments MS and OR intersect at T, and $m\angle N = 40°$.

06 2017 17

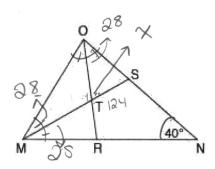

If $m\angle TMR = 28°$, the measure of angle OTS is

?

1)   40º   2)   50º

3)   60º   4)   70º

5

4. In the diagram below, $\overline{DE}$ divides
   $\overline{AB}$ and $\overline{AC}$ proportionally, $m\angle C = 26°$,
   $m\angle A = 82°$, and $\overline{DF}$ bisects $\angle BDE$.

06 2017 10

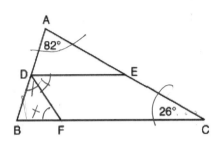

The measure of angle DFB is

1)   36°   2)   54°

3)   72°   4)   82°

5. In the diagram below, $m\angle BDC = 100°$,
   $m\angle A = 50°$, and $m\angle DBC = 30°$.

08 2016 04

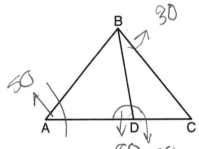

Which statement is true?

1) $\triangle ABD$ is obtuse. ✓
2) $\triangle ABC$ is isosceles. ✗
3) $m\angle ABD = 80°$
4) $\triangle ABD$ is scalene.

6. An equilateral triangle has sides of length 20. To the *nearest tenth*, what is the height of the equilateral triangle?

08 2016 08

1) 10.0   2) 11.5

3) 17.3   4) 23.1

$a^2 + b^2 = c^2$

7. Line segment *EA* is the perpendicular bisector of $\overline{ZT}$, and $\overline{ZE}$ and $\overline{TE}$ are drawn.

06 2016 19

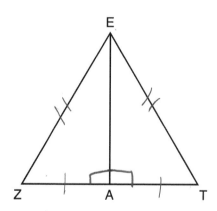

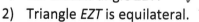

Which conclusion can *not* be proven?

1) $\overline{EA}$ bisects angle *ZET*. ✓
2) Triangle *EZT* is equilateral. ✓
3) $\overline{EA}$ is a median of triangle *EZT*.
4) Angle *Z* is congruent to angle *T*.

7

8. The coordinates of the vertices of $\triangle RST$ are $R(-2,-3)$, $S(8,2)$, and $T(4,5)$.
Which type of triangle is $\triangle RST$?

01 2016 18

1) right
2) acute
3) obtuse
4) equiangular

9. The ratio of similarity of $\triangle BOY$ to $\triangle GRL$ is $1:2$. If $BO = x+3$ and $GR = 3x - 1$, then the length of $\overline{GR}$ is

01 2016 20

1) 5
2) 7
3) 10
4) 20

10. In the diagram below, $\overline{CD}$ is the altitude drawn to the hypotenuse $\overline{AB}$ of right triangle ABC.

01 2016 22

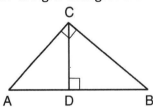

8

Which lengths would *not* produce an altitude that measures $6\sqrt{2}$?

1) $AD = 2$ and $DB = 36$
2) $AD = 3$ and $AB = 24$
3) $AD = 6$ and $DB = 12$
4) $AD = 8$ and $AB = 17$

11. In $\triangle SCU$ shown below, points T and O are on $\overline{SU}$ and $\overline{CU}$, respectively. Segment OT is drawn so that $\angle C \cong \angle OTU$.

01 2016 24

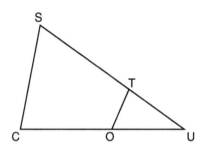

If $TU = 4$, $OU = 5$, and $OC = 7$, what is the length of $\overline{ST}$?

1) 5.6   2) 8.75

3) 11   4) 15

12. Given the theorem, "The sum of the measures of the interior angles of a triangle is 180°," complete the proof for this theorem.

01 2016 33

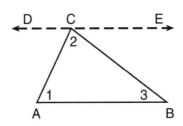

Given: $\triangle ABC$
Prove: $m\angle 1 + m\angle 2 + m\angle 3 = 180°$
Fill in the missing reasons below.

Statements	Reasons
(1) $\triangle ABC$	(1) Given
(2) Through point C, draw $\overleftrightarrow{DCE}$ parallel to $\overline{AB}$.	(2) _____
(3) $m\angle 1 = m\angle ACD$, $m\angle 3 = m\angle BCE$	(3) _____
(4) $m\angle ACD + m\angle 2 + m\angle BCE = 180°$	(4) _____
(5) $m\angle 1 + m\angle 2 + m\angle 3 = 180°$	(5) _____

13. In the diagram of parallelogram
FRED shown below, $\overline{ED}$ is extended
to A, and $\overline{AF}$ is drawn such that $\overline{AF} \cong \overline{DF}$.

08 2015 08

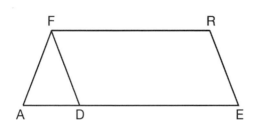

If $m\angle R = 124°$, what is $m\angle AFD$?

   1) 124°
   2) 112°
   3) 68°
   4) 56°

14. Linda is designing a circular piece of
stained glass with a diameter of 7 inches.
She is going to sketch a square inside the
circular region. To the *nearest tenth of an
inch*, the largest possible length of a side
of the square is

08 2015 11

   1) 3.5
   2) 4.9
   3) 5.0
   4) 6.9

11

15. In the diagram below, the line of sight from the park ranger station, *P*, to the lifeguard chair, *L*, on the beach of a lake is perpendicular to the path joining the campground, *C*, and the first aid station, *F*. The campground is 0.25 mile from the lifeguard chair. The straight paths from both the campground and first aid station to the park ranger station are perpendicular.

06 2015 34

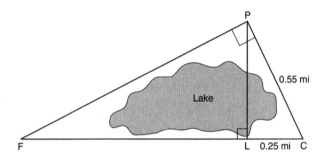

If the path from the park ranger station to the campground is 0.55 mile, determine and state, to the *nearest hundredth of a mile*, the distance between the park ranger station and the lifeguard chair. Gerald believes the distance from the first aid station to the campground is at least 1.5 miles. Is Gerald correct? Justify your answer.

Constructions

1. Using a compass and straightedge, construct a regular hexagon inscribed in circle *O*. [Leave all construction marks.]

   08 2017 28

   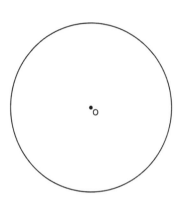

2. Given: Trapezoid *JKLM* with $\overline{JK} \parallel \overline{ML}$
   Using a compass and straightedge, construct the altitude from vertex *J* to $\overline{ML}$. [Leave all construction marks.]

   06 2017 25

   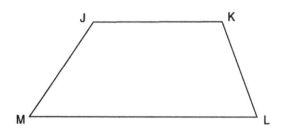

3. In the diagram of △ABC shown
   below, use a compass and straightedge
   to construct the median to AB.
   [Leave all construction marks.]

08 2016 28

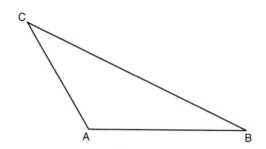

4. Using a compass and straightedge,
   construct and label △A'B'C', the
   image of △ABC after a dilation with
   a scale factor of 2 and centered at B.
   [Leave all construction marks.]
   Describe the relationship between the
   lengths of AC and A'C'.

08 2016 32

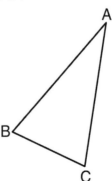

5. In the diagram below, radius $\overline{OA}$ is
    drawn in circle O. Using a compass
    and a straightedge, construct a line
    tangent to circle O at point A.
    [Leave all construction marks.]

06 2016 31

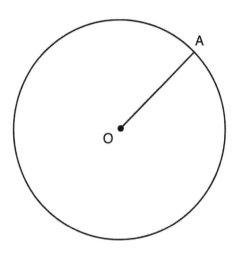

6. Triangle *XYZ* is shown below. Using a compass and straightedge, on the line below, construct and label $\triangle ABC$, such that $\triangle ABC \cong \triangle XYZ$. [Leave all construction marks.] Based on your construction, state the theorem that justifies why $\triangle ABC$ is congruent to $\triangle XYZ$.

01 2016 34

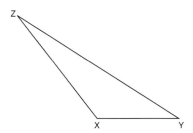

7. Construct an equilateral triangle
inscribed in circle *T* shown below.
[Leave all construction marks.]

08 2015 26

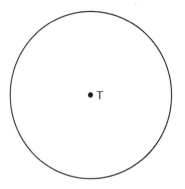

• T

8. Use a compass and straightedge
to construct an inscribed square
in circle *T* shown below.
[Leave all construction marks.]

06 2015 25

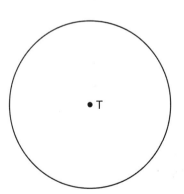

• T

Transformations

1. The coordinates of the endpoints of
$\overline{AB}$ are $A(2, 3)$ and $B(5, -1)$. Determine
the length of $\overline{A'B'}$, the image of $\overline{AB}$, after
a dilation of $\frac{1}{2}$ centered at the origin.

[The use of the set of axes below is optional.]

08 2017 29

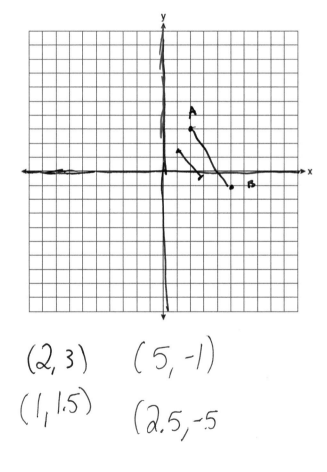

$(2, 3)$ $(5, -1)$

$(1, 1.5)$ $(2.5, -5$

2. Quadrilateral *MATH* and its image
   M"A"T"H" are graphed on the set of
   axes below.

08 2017 27

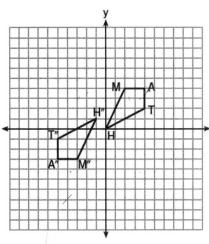

A rotation
of 180°
counter
clockwise

Describe a sequence of transformations that maps
quadrilateral *MATH* onto quadrilateral *M"A"T"H"*.

3. A regular decagon is rotated *n* degrees
   about its center, carrying the decagon
   onto itself. The value of *n* could be

   08 2017 22

   1) 10° $\ln = 360$ 3) 225°

   2) 150° 4) 252°

4. The line represented by the equation
   $4y = 3x + 7$ is transformed by a dilation
   centered at the origin. Which linear
   equation could represent its image?

   08 2017 10

   1) $3x - 4y = 9$ 3) $4x - 3y = 9$

   2) $3x + 4y = 9$ 4) $4x + 3y = 9$

5   As shown in the graph below, the quadrilateral is a rectangle.

08 2017 06

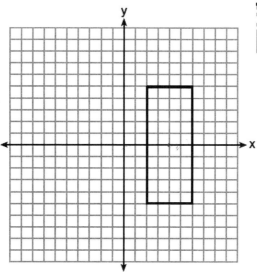

Which transformation would *not* map the rectangle onto itself?

1) a reflection over the *x*-axis

2) a reflection over the line $x = 4$

3) a rotation of 180° about the origin

4) a rotation of 180° about the point $(4, 0)$

6.   The image of $\triangle DEF$ is $\triangle D'E'F'$. Under which transformation will the triangles *not* be congruent?

08 2017 02

1) a reflection through the
   origin

2) a reflection over the line
   $y = x$

3) a dilation with a scale
   factor of 1 centered at
   $(2, 3)$

4) a dilation with a scale
   factor of $\frac{3}{2}$ centered at
   the origin

7. Triangle ABC has vertices at $A(-5, 2)$, $B(-4, 7)$,
   and $C(-2, 7)$, and triangle DEF has vertices at
   $D(3, 2)$, $E(2, 7)$, and $F(0, 7)$. Graph and label
   $\triangle ABC$ and $\triangle DEF$ on the set of axes below.
   Determine and state the single
   transformation where $\triangle DEF$ is the image
   of $\triangle ABC$. Use your transformation to
   explain why $\triangle ABC \cong \triangle DEF$.

06 2017 32

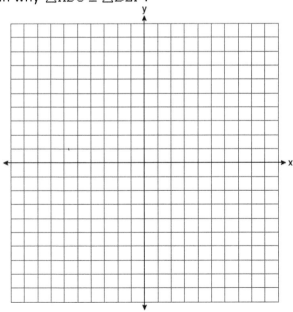

8. Line *n* is represented by the equation $3x + 4y = 20$. Determine and state the equation of line *p*, the image of line *n*, after a dilation of scale factor $\frac{1}{3}$ centered at the point $(4, 2)$. [The use of the set of axes below is optional.] Explain your answer.

06 2017 31

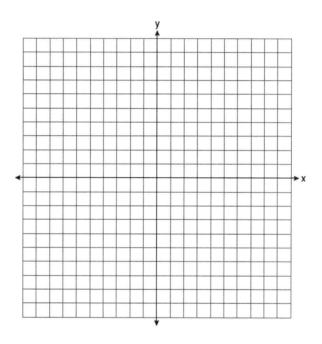

9. Triangle *ABC* and triangle *DEF* are
drawn below.

06 2017 30

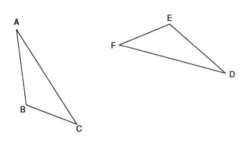

If $\overline{AB} \cong \overline{DE}$, $\overline{AC} \cong \overline{DF}$, and $\angle A \cong \angle D$, write a sequence of
transformations that maps triangle *ABC* onto triangle *DEF*.

10. In the two distinct acute triangles *ABC* and
DEF, $\angle B \cong \angle E$. Triangles *ABC* and *DEF* are
congruent when there is a sequence of rigid
motions that maps

06 2017 22

1) $\angle A$ onto $\angle D$, and $\angle C$ onto $\angle F$
2) $\overline{AC}$ onto $\overline{DF}$, and $\overline{BC}$ onto $\overline{EF}$
3) $\angle C$ onto $\angle F$, and $\overline{BC}$ onto $\overline{EF}$
4) point *A* onto point *D*, and $\overline{AB}$ onto $\overline{DE}$

11. Triangle $A'B'C'$ is the image of $\triangle ABC$
after a dilation followed by a translation.
Which statement(s) would always be true
with respect to this sequence of
transformations?

06 2017 14

I. $\triangle ABC \cong \triangle A'B'C'$
II. $\triangle ABC \sim \triangle A'B'C'$
III. $\overline{AB} \parallel \overline{A'B'}$
IV. $AA' = BB'$

23

1) II, only
2) I and II
3) II and III
4) II, III, and IV

12. Which figure always has exactly four lines
    of reflection that map the figure onto itself?

06 2017 07

1) square
2) rectangle
3) regular octagon
4) equilateral triangle

13. A line segment is dilated by a scale factor
    of 2 centered at a point not on the line
    segment. Which statement regarding the
    relationship between the given line
    segment and its image is true?

06 2017 06

1) The line segments are perpendicular, and
   the image is one-half of the length of the
   given line segment.
2) The line segments are perpendicular, and
   the image is twice the length of the given
   line segment.
3) The line segments are parallel, and the
   image is twice the length of the given line
   segment.
4) The line segments are parallel, and the
   image is one-half of the length of the given
   line segment.

24

14. In the diagram below, $\triangle ABC \cong \triangle DEF$.

06 2017 01

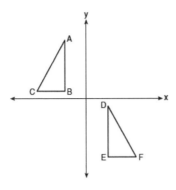

Which sequence of transformations maps
$\triangle ABC$ onto $\triangle DEF$?

1) a reflection over the x-axis followed by a
   translation
2) a reflection over the y-axis followed by a
   translation
3) a rotation of 180° about the origin followed
   by a translation
4) a counterclockwise rotation of 90° about
   the origin followed by a translation

15. Which transformation would *not*
always produce an image that would
be congruent to the original figure?

08 2016 02

1) translation
2) dilation
3) rotation
4) Reflection

25

16. Which point shown in the graph below is the image of point *P* after a counterclockwise rotation of 90° about the origin?

08 2016 05

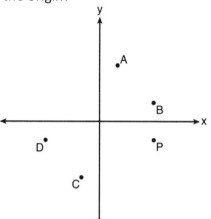

1) *A*
2) *B*
3) *C*
4) *D*

17. Given: $\triangle AEC$, $\triangle DEF$, and $\overline{FE} \perp \overline{CE}$

08 2016 09

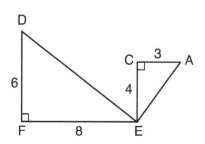

What is a correct sequence of similarity transformations that shows $\triangle AEC \sim \triangle DEF$?

1) a rotation of 180 degrees about point *E* followed by a horizontal translation
2) a counterclockwise rotation of 90 degrees about point *E* followed by a horizontal translation
3) a rotation of 180 degrees about point *E* followed by a dilation with a scale factor of 2 centered at point *E*
4) a counterclockwise rotation of 90 degrees about point *E* followed by a dilation with a scale factor of 2 centered at point *E*

08 2016 26

18. In the diagram below, $\triangle ABC$ has coordinates $A(1, 1)$, $B(4, 1)$, and $C(4, 5)$. Graph and label $\triangle A''B''C''$, the image of $\triangle ABC$ after the translation five units to the right and two units up followed by the reflection over the line $y = 0$.

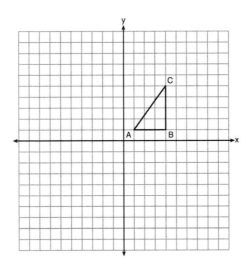

19. A regular hexagon is rotated in a counterclockwise direction about its center. Determine and state the minimum number of degrees in the rotation such that the hexagon will coincide with itself.

08 2016 27

20. Triangle *MNP* is the image of triangle *JKL* after a 120° counterclockwise rotation about point *Q*. If the measure of angle *L* is 47° and the measure of angle *N* is 57°, determine the measure of angle *M*. Explain how you arrived at your answer.

08 2016 29

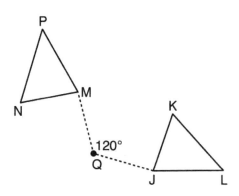

21. The grid below shows △ABC and △DEF.

08 2016 33a

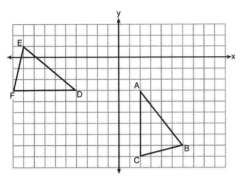

Let △A'B'C' be the image of △ABC after a rotation about point A. Determine and state the location of B' if the location of point C' is (8, −3). Explain your answer. Is △DEF congruent to △A'B'C'? Explain your answer.

22. Which transformation of $\overline{OA}$ would result in an image parallel to $\overline{OA}$?

06 2016 04

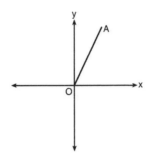

1) a translation of two units down
2) a reflection over the x-axis
3) a reflection over the y-axis
4) a clockwise rotation of 90° about the origin

23. Which sequence of transformations
will map △ABC onto △A'B'C'?

06 2016 08

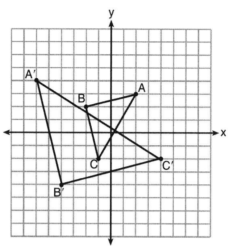

1) reflection and translation
2) rotation and reflection
3) translation and dilation
4) dilation and rotation

24. On the set of axes below, rectangle
ABCD can be proven congruent to
rectangle KLMN using which transformation?

06 2016 16

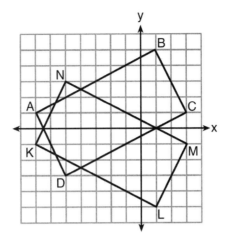

1) rotation
2) translation
3) reflection over the x-axis
4) reflection over the y-axis

25. Describe a sequence of transformations that will map $\triangle ABC$ onto $\triangle DEF$ as shown below.

06 2016 25

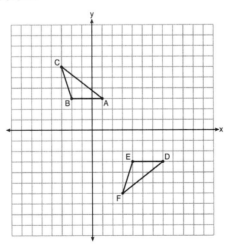

26. In the diagram below, $\triangle A'B'C'$ is the image of $\triangle ABC$ after a transformation.

06 2016 34

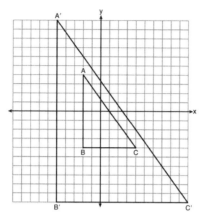

Describe the transformation that was performed. Explain why $\triangle A'B'C' \sim \triangle ABC$.

27. Which transformation would result in the perimeter of a triangle being different from the perimeter of its image?

01 2016 05

1) $(x,y) \rightarrow (y,x)$
2) $(x,y) \rightarrow (x,-y)$
3) $(x,y) \rightarrow (4x,4y)$
4) $(x,y) \rightarrow (x+2,y-5)$

28. Triangle *ABC* and triangle *DEF* are graphed on the set of axes below.

01 2016 08

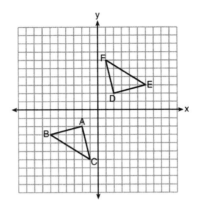

Which sequence of transformations maps triangle *ABC* onto triangle *DEF*?

1) a reflection over the x-axis followed by a reflection over the y-axis
2) a 180° rotation about the origin followed by a reflection over the line $y = x$
3) a 90° clockwise rotation about the origin followed by a reflection over the y-axis
4) a translation 8 units to the right and 1 unit up followed by a 90° counterclockwise rotation about the origin

29. A line that passes through the points whose coordinates are $(1, 1)$ and $(5, 7)$ is dilated by a scale factor of 3 and centered at the origin. The image of the line

01 2016 10

1) is perpendicular to the original line
2) is parallel to the original line
3) passes through the origin
4) is the original line

33

30. Quadrilateral *ABCD* is graphed on the set of axes below.

01 2016 11

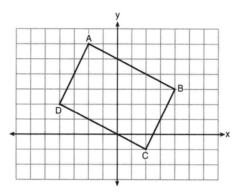

When *ABCD* is rotated 90° in a counterclockwise direction about the origin, its image is quadrilateral *A'B'C'D'*. Is distance preserved under this rotation, and which coordinates are correct for the given vertex?

1) no and $C'(1,2)$
2) no and $D'(2,4)$
3) yes and $A'(6,2)$
4) yes and $B'(-3,4)$

31. Triangle *ABC* is graphed on the set of axes below. Graph and label $\triangle A'B'C'$, the image of $\triangle ABC$ after a reflection over the line $x = 1$.

01 2016 25

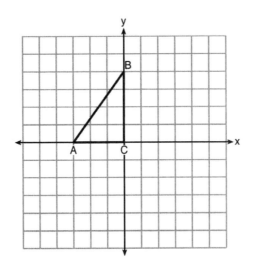

32. The image of $\triangle ABC$ after a dilation of scale factor k centered at point A is $\triangle ADE$, as shown in the diagram below.

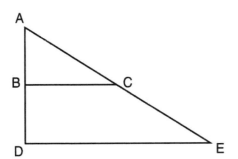

Which statement is always true?

1) $2AB = AD$
2) $\overline{AD} \perp \overline{DE}$
3) $AC = CE$
4) $\overline{BC} \parallel \overline{DE}$

33. A sequence of transformations maps rectangle *ABCD* onto rectangle *A"B"C"D"*, as shown in the diagram below.

08 2015 07

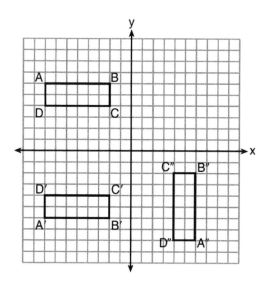

Which sequence of transformations maps *ABCD* onto *A'B'C'D'* and then maps *A'B'C'D'* onto *A"B"C"D"*?

1) a reflection followed by a rotation
2) a reflection followed by a translation
3) a translation followed by a rotation
4) a translation followed by a reflection

34. In the diagram below, which single transformation was used to map triangle *A* onto triangle *B*?

08 2015 13

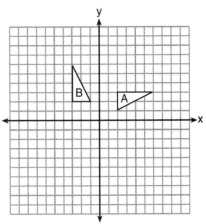

1) line reflection
2) rotation
3) dilation
4) translation

35. A triangle is dilated by a scale factor of 3 with the center of dilation at the origin. Which statement is true?

08 2015 20

1) The area of the image is nine times the area of the original triangle.
2) The perimeter of the image is nine times the perimeter of the original triangle.
3) The slope of any side of the image is three times the slope of the corresponding side of the original triangle.
4) The measure of each angle in the image is three times the measure of the corresponding angle of the original triangle.

37

36. In the diagram below, $\overline{AC} \cong \overline{DF}$ and
    Points A, C, D, and F are collinear on line ℓ.

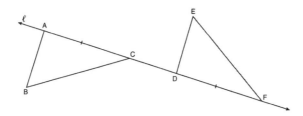

Let $\triangle D'E'F'$ be the image of $\triangle DEF$ after a translation along ℓ, such that point D is mapped onto point A. Determine and state the location of F'. Explain your answer.

Let $\triangle D''E''F''$ be the image of $\triangle D'E'F'$ after a reflection across line ℓ. Suppose that E'' is located at B. Is $\triangle DEF$ congruent to $\triangle ABC$? Explain your answer.

37. The vertices of $\triangle JKL$ have coordinates $J(5,1)$, $K(-2,-3)$, and $L(-4,1)$. Under which transformation is the image $\triangle J'K'L'$ not congruent to $\triangle JKL$?

1) a translation of two units to the right and two units down
2) a counterclockwise rotation of 180 degrees around the origin
3) a reflection over the x-axis
4) a dilation with a scale factor of 2 and centered at the origin

38. In the diagram below, congruent figures
1, 2, and 3 are drawn.

06 2015 04

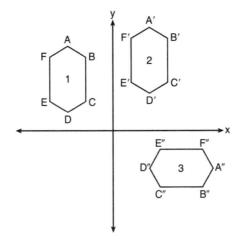

Which sequence of transformations maps figure 1 onto
figure 2 and then figure 2 onto figure 3?

1) a reflection followed by a translation
2) a rotation followed by a translation
3) a translation followed by a reflection
4) a translation followed by a rotation

39. Which regular polygon has a minimum
rotation of 45° to carry the polygon
onto itself?

06 2015 10

1) octagon
2) decagon
3) hexagon
4) pentagon

40. If $\triangle ABC$ is dilated by a scale factor of 3, which statement is true of the image $\triangle A'B'C'$?

06 2015 16

  1) $3A'B' = AB$
  2) $B'C' = 3BC$
  3) $m\angle A' = 3(m\angle A)$
  4) $3(m\angle C') = m\angle C$

41. Given: Quadrilateral ABCD is a parallelogram with diagonals $\overline{AC}$ and $\overline{BD}$ intersecting at E

06 2015 33

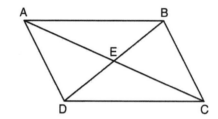

Prove: $\triangle AED \cong \triangle CEB$
Describe a single rigid motion that maps $\triangle AED$ onto $\triangle CEB$.

42. As graphed on the set of axes below, △$A'B'C'$ is the image of △ABC after a sequence of transformations.

01 2016 28

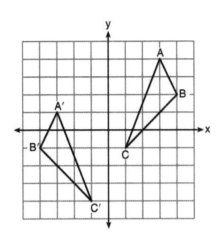

Is △$A'B'C'$ congruent to △ABC? Use the properties of rigid motion to explain your answer.

43. Line ℓ is mapped onto line m by a dilation centered at the origin with a scale factor of 2. The equation of line ℓ is $3x - y = 4$. Determine and state an equation for line m.

01 2016 31

44. In the diagram below, a square is graphed in the coordinate plane.

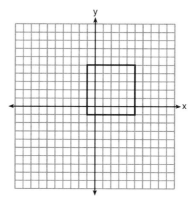

A reflection over which line does *not* carry the square onto itself?

1) $x = 5$
2) $y = 2$
3) $y = x$
4) $x + y = 4$

45. In the diagram below, $\triangle ABE$ is the image of $\triangle ACD$ after a dilation centered at the origin. The coordinates of the vertices are $A(0,0)$, $B(3,0)$, $C(4.5,0)$, $D(0,6)$, and $E(0,4)$.

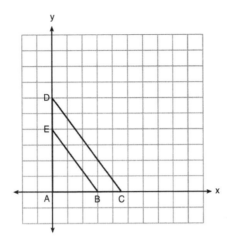

The ratio of the lengths of $\overline{BE}$ to $\overline{CD}$ is

1) $\dfrac{2}{3}$

2) $\dfrac{3}{2}$

3) $\dfrac{3}{4}$

4) $\dfrac{4}{3}$

46. Line $y = 3x - 1$ is transformed by a dilation with a scale factor of 2 and centered at $(3, 8)$. The line's image is

08 2015 24

1) $y = 3x - 8$
2) $y = 3x - 4$
3) $y = 3x - 2$
4) $y = 3x - 1$

47. In the diagram below, $\overline{CD}$ is the image of $\overline{AB}$ after a dilation of scale factor k with center E.

06 2015 18

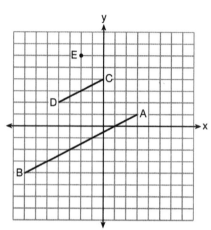

Which ratio is equal to the scale factor k of the dilation?

1) $\dfrac{EC}{EA}$ 2) $\dfrac{BA}{EA}$

3) $\dfrac{EA}{BA}$ 4) $\dfrac{EA}{EC}$

48. The line $3y = -2x + 8$ is transformed by a dilation centered at the origin. Which linear equation could be its image?

06 2015 22

1) $2x + 3y = 5$
2) $2x - 3y = 5$
3) $3x + 2y = 5$
4) $3x - 2y = 5$

Triangle Congruence

1   Given: $\overline{RS}$ and $\overline{TV}$ bisect each other
    at point X $\overline{TR}$ and $\overline{SV}$ are drawn

06 2017 33

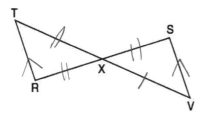

Prove: $\overline{TR} \parallel \overline{SV}$

2   Kelly is completing a proof based on
    the figure below.

06 2017 09

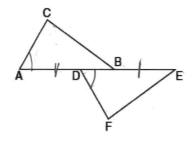

She was given that $\angle A \cong \angle EDF$, and has already proven
$\overline{AB} \cong \overline{DE}$. Which pair of corresponding parts and triangle
congruency method would *not* prove $\triangle ABC \cong \triangle DEF$?

1) $\overline{AC} \cong \overline{DF}$ and SAS

2) $\overline{BC} \cong \overline{EF}$ and SAS

3) $\angle C \cong \angle F$ and AAS ✓

3   Two right triangles must be congruent if

06 2016 07

1)   an acute angle in each triangle is congruent
2)   the lengths of the hypotenuses are equal
3)   the corresponding legs are congruent
4)   the areas are equal

4   Given: Quadrilateral *ABCD* with
        diagonals $\overline{AC}$ and $\overline{BD}$ that bisect
        each other, and $\angle 1 \cong \angle 2$

06 2016 35

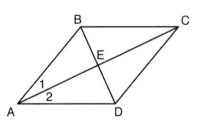

Prove: $\triangle ACD$ is an isosceles triangle and $\triangle AEB$
is a right triangle

5   If $\triangle A'B'C'$ is the image of $\triangle ABC$,
        under which transformation will the
        triangles *not* be congruent?

08 2015 02

1)   reflection over the *x*-axis
2)   translation to the left 5 and down 4
3)   dilation centered at the origin with
     scale factor 2
4)   rotation of 270° counterclockwise
     about the origin

46

6   In the diagram below, $\triangle ABC$ and
    $\triangle XYZ$ are graphed.

08 2015 30

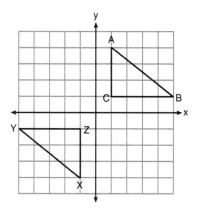

Use the properties of rigid motions to explain why
$\triangle ABC \cong \triangle XYZ$.

7   In the diagram below, $\overline{AC} \cong \overline{DF}$ and
    points A, C, D, and F are collinear on line ℓ.

08 2015 34

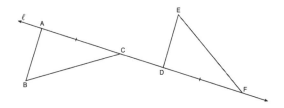

Let $\triangle D'E'F'$ be the image of $\triangle DEF$ after a translation
along ℓ, such that point D is mapped onto point A.
Determine and state the location of F'. Explain your
answer.

Let $\triangle D''E''F''$ be the image of $\triangle D'E'F'$ after a reflection
across line ℓ. Suppose that E'' is located at B. Is $\triangle DEF$
congruent to $\triangle ABC$? Explain your answer.

8   Which statement is sufficient evidence
     that △DEF is congruent to △ABC ?

06 2015 24

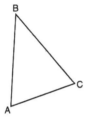 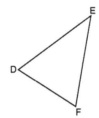

1) AB = DE and BC = EF
2) ∠D ≅ ∠A, ∠B ≅ ∠E, ∠C ≅ ∠F
3) There is a sequence of rigid motions that
    maps $\overline{AB}$ onto $\overline{DE}$, $\overline{BC}$ onto $\overline{EF}$, and $\overline{AC}$
    onto $\overline{DF}$.
4) There is a sequence of rigid motions that
    maps point A onto point D, $\overline{AB}$ onto $\overline{DE}$,
    and ∠B onto ∠E.

9   After a reflection over a line, △A'B'C'
     is the image of triangle ABC. Explain why
     triangle ABC is congruent to triangle △A'B'C'.

06 2015 30

Circles, Lines and Segments on the Coordinate Plane

1 What is an equation of the perpendicular bisector of the line segment shown in the diagram below?

08 2017 24

1) $y + 2x = 0$

2) $y - 2x = 0$

3) $2y + x = 0$

4) $2y - x = 0$

2 The coordinates of the endpoints of $\overline{AB}$ are $A(-8,-2)$ and $B(16,6)$. Point P is on $\overline{AB}$. What are the coordinates of point P, such that $AP:PB$ is 3:5?

1) $(1,1)$ 3) $(9.6, 3.6)$

2) $(7,3)$ 4) $(6.4, 2.8)$

3 In the diagram below of circle O, chord $\overline{CD}$ is parallel to diameter $\overline{AOB}$ and $m\overparen{CD} = 130$.

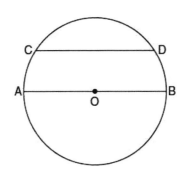

What is $m\overparen{AC}$?

1) 25   3) 65
2) 50   4) 115

4 The vertices of square *RSTV* have
   coordinates $R(-1, 5)$, $S(-3, 1)$, $T(-7, 3)$,
   and $V(-5, 7)$.
   What is the perimeter of *RSTV*?

08 2017 03

1) $\sqrt{20}$ 3) $4\sqrt{20}$

2) $\sqrt{40}$ 4) $4\sqrt{40}$

5 What is an equation of a line that is
   perpendicular to the line whose equation
   is $2y = 3x - 10$ and passes through $(-6, 1)$?

06 2017 19

1) $y = -\frac{2}{3}x - 5$

2) $y = -\frac{2}{3}x - 3$

3) $y = \frac{2}{3}x + 1$

4) $y = \frac{2}{3}x + 10$

6 Line segment *RW* has endpoints $R(-4, 5)$
   and $W(6, 20)$. Point *P* is on $\overline{RW}$ such that
   $RP:PW$ is 2:3. What are the coordinates
   of point *P*?

06 2017 15

1) $(2, 9)$

2) $(0, 11)$

3) $(2, 14)$

4) $(10, 2)$

7 The equation of a circle is
$x^2 + y^2 - 12y + 20 = 0$.
What are the coordinates of the center and
the length of the radius of the circle?

06 2017 12

1) center $(0, 6)$ and radius 4
2) center $(0, -6)$ and radius 4
3) center $(0, 6)$ and radius 16
4) center $(0, -6)$ and radius 16

8 On the set of axes below, the vertices of
$\triangle PQR$ have coordinates $P(-6, 7)$, $Q(2, 1)$,
and $R(-1, -3)$.

06 2017 02

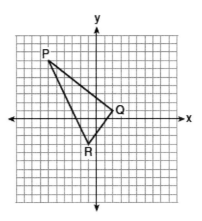

What is the area of $\triangle PQR$?

1) 10
2) 20
3) 25
4) 50

52

9   The diagonals of rhombus *TEAM*
     intersect at $P(2,1)$. If the equation of the
     line that contains diagonal $\overline{TA}$ is $y = -x + 3$,
     what is the equation of a line that contains
     diagonal *EM*?

08 2016 14

1) $y = x - 1$ 2) $y = x - 3$

3) $y = -x - 1$ 4) $y = -x - 3$

10   The coordinates of vertices *A* and *B*
     of $\triangle ABC$ are $A(3,4)$ and $B(3,12)$.
     If the area of $\triangle ABC$ is 24 square units,
     what could be the coordinates of point *C*?

08 2016 15

1)   (3, 6)   2)   (8, –3)

3)   (–3, 8)   4)   (6, 3)

11   What are the coordinates of the center and
     the length of the radius of the circle
     represented by the equation
     $x^2 + y^2 - 4x + 8y + 11 = 0$?

08 2016 16

1) center $(2,-4)$ and radius 3
2) center $(-2,4)$ and radius 3
3) center $(2,-4)$ and radius 9
4) center $(-2,4)$ and radius 9

12   Point *P* is on the directed line
      segment from point $X(-6, -2)$ to
      point $Y(6, 7)$ and divides the segment
      in the ratio $1:5$.
      What are the coordinates of point *P*?

08 2016 18

1) $\left(4, 5\frac{1}{2}\right)$ 2) $\left(-\frac{1}{2}, -4\right)$

3) $\left(-4\frac{1}{2}, 0\right)$ 4) $\left(-4, -\frac{1}{2}\right)$

13   Line segment $A'B'$, whose
      endpoints are $(4, -2)$ and $(16, 14)$,
      is the image of $\overline{AB}$ after a dilation
      of $\frac{1}{2}$ centered at the origin.
      What is the length of $\overline{AB}$?

08 2016 21

1)   5   2)   10

3)   20   4)   40

14   A circle has a center at $(1, -2)$ and
      radius of 4. Does the point $(3.4, 1.2)$
      lie on the circle? Justify your answer.

08 2016 30

15   Kevin's work for deriving the equation
of a circle is shown below.

06 2016 03

$$x^2 + 4x = -(y^2 - 20)$$

STEP 1 $x^2 + 4x = -y^2 + 20$

STEP 2 $x^2 + 4x + 4 = -y^2 + 20 - 4$

STEP 3 $(x + 2)^2 = -y^2 + 20 - 4$

STEP 4 $(x + 2)^2 + y^2 = 16$

In which step did he make an error in his work?

1) Step 1
2) Step 2
3) Step 3
4) Step 4

16   A company is creating an object
from a wooden cube with an edge
length of 8.5 cm. A right circular cone
with a diameter of 8 cm and an altitude
of 8 cm will be cut out of the cube.
Which expression represents the volume
of the remaining wood?

06 2016 06

1) $(8.5)^3 - \pi(8)^2(8)$

2) $(8.5)^3 - \pi(4)^2(8)$

3) $(8.5)^3 - \frac{1}{3}\pi(8)^2(8)$

4) $(8.5)^3 - \frac{1}{3}\pi(4)^2(8)$

17 Line segment NY has endpoints $N(-11, 5)$ and $Y(5, -7)$. What is the equation of the perpendicular bisector of $\overline{NY}$?

06 2016 12

1) $y + 1 = \frac{4}{3}(x + 3)$

2) $y + 1 = -\frac{3}{4}(x + 3)$

3) $y - 6 = \frac{4}{3}(x - 8)$

4) $y - 6 = -\frac{3}{4}(x - 8)$

18 In the diagram below, $\triangle ABC$ has vertices $A(4, 5)$, $B(2, 1)$, and $C(7, 3)$.

06 2016 14

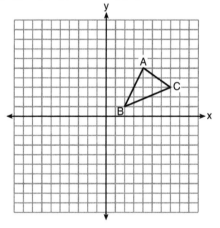

What is the slope of the altitude drawn from A to $\overline{BC}$?

1) $\frac{2}{5}$ 2) $\frac{3}{2}$

3) $-\frac{1}{2}$ 4) $-\frac{5}{2}$

19   Triangle *RST* is graphed on the
     set of axes below.

06 2016 22

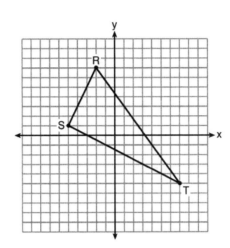

How many square units are in the area of $\triangle RST$?

1) $9\sqrt{3} + 15$
2) $9\sqrt{5} + 15$
3)   45
4)   90

20   The graph below shows $\overline{AB}$, which 06 2016 23
is a chord of circle O. The coordinates
of the endpoints of $\overline{AB}$ are $A(3,3)$ and
$B(3,-7)$. The distance from the midpoint
of $\overline{AB}$ to the center of circle O is 2 units.

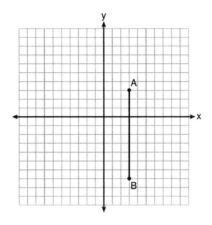

What could be a correct equation for circle O?

1) $(x-1)^2 + (y+2)^2 = 29$
2) $(x+5)^2 + (y-2)^2 = 29$
3) $(x-1)^2 + (y-2)^2 = 25$
4) $(x-5)^2 + (y+2)^2 = 25$

06 2016 26

21   Point P is on segment AB such that
$AP:PB$ is $4:5$. If A has coordinates
$(4,2)$, and B has coordinates $(22,2)$,
determine and state the coordinates of P.

22   An equation of a line perpendicular
     to the line represented by the equation

     $y = -\frac{1}{2}x - 5$ and passing through $(6, -4)$ is

1) $y = -\frac{1}{2}x + 4$ 2) $y = -\frac{1}{2}x - 1$

3) $y = 2x + 14$ 4) $y = 2x - 16$

23   The endpoints of one side of a regular
     pentagon are $(-1, 4)$ and $(2, 3)$. What is
     the perimeter of the pentagon?

   1) $\sqrt{10}$
   2) $5\sqrt{10}$
   3) $5\sqrt{2}$
   4) $25\sqrt{2}$

24   Directed line segment PT has
     endpoints whose coordinates are
     $P(-2, 1)$ and $T(4, 7)$. Determine the
     coordinates of point J that divides the
     segment in the ratio 2 to 1.
     [The use of the set of axes below is optional.]

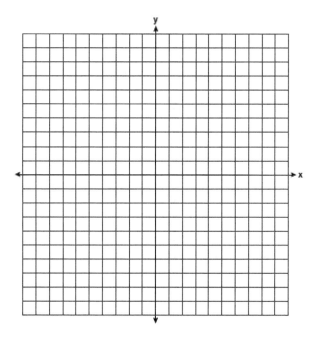

25   If $x^2 + 4x + y^2 - 6y - 12 = 0$ is the
equation of a circle, the length of
the radius is

08 2015 09

1) 25
2) 16
3) 5
4) 4

26   Given $\overline{MN}$ shown below, with $M(-6,1)$ and $N(3,-5)$, what is an equation of the line that passes through point $P(6,1)$ and is parallel to $\overline{MN}$?

08 2015 10

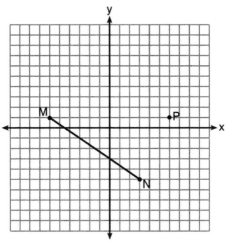

1), $y = -\dfrac{2}{3}x + 5$ 2), $y = -\dfrac{2}{3}x - 3$

3), $y = \dfrac{3}{2}x + 7$ 4), $y = \dfrac{3}{2}x - 8$

27   The endpoints of $\overline{DEF}$ are $D(1,4)$ and $F(16,14)$. Determine and state the coordinates of point E, if $DE{:}EF = 2{:}3$.

08 2015 31

28   The center of circle Q has coordinates
$(3,-2)$. If circle Q passes through $R(7,1)$,
what is the length of its diameter?

06 2015 03

1) 50
2) 25
3) 10
4)   5

29   Which equation represents a line that
is perpendicular to the line represented
by $2x - y = 7$?

06 2015 09

1) $y = -\dfrac{1}{2}x + 6$

2) $y = \dfrac{1}{2}x + 6$

3) $y = -2x + 6$
4) $y = 2x + 6$

30   The equation of a circle is
$x^2 + y^2 + 6y = 7$. What are the
coordinates of the center and
the length of the radius of the circle?

06 2015 14

1) center $(0,3)$ and radius 4
2) center $(0,-3)$ and radius 4
3) center $(0,3)$ and radius 16
4) center $(0,-3)$ and radius 16

62

31   The coordinates of the endpoints of   06 2015 27
     $\overline{AB}$ are $A(-6,-5)$ and $B(4,0)$.

     Point P is on $\overline{AB}$. Determine and state
     the coordinates of point P, such that
     $AP:PB$ is $2:3$.
     [The use of the set of axes below is optional.]

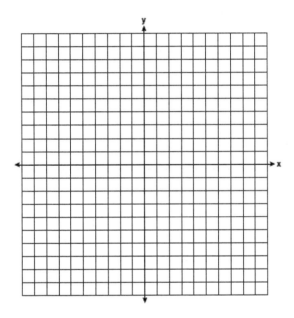

Circles

1 In the diagram below of circle O, tangent $\overleftrightarrow{EC}$ is drawn to diameter $\overline{AC}$. Chord $\overline{BC}$ is parallel to secant $\overline{ADE}$, and chord $\overline{AB}$ is drawn.

08 2017 33

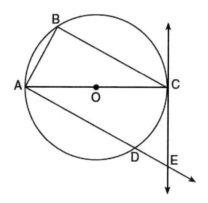

Prove: $\dfrac{BC}{CA} = \dfrac{AB}{EC}$

2 Determine and state the coordinates of the center and the length of the radius of a circle whose equation is $x^2 + y^2 - 6x = 56 - 8y$.

08 2017 31

3 In a circle with a diameter of 32, the area
of a sector is $\dfrac{512\pi}{3}$. The measure of the
angle of the sector, in radians, is

1) $\dfrac{\pi}{3}$ 3) $\dfrac{16\pi}{3}$

2) $\dfrac{4\pi}{3}$ 4) $\dfrac{64\pi}{3}$

4 In the diagram shown below, $\overline{PA}$ is
tangent to circle T at A, and secant $\overline{PBC}$ is
drawn where point B is on circle T.

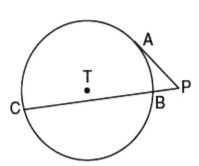

If $PB = 3$ and $BC = 15$, what is the length of $\overline{PA}$?

1) $3\sqrt{5}$ 3) 3

2) $3\sqrt{6}$ 4) 9

5 Determine and state, in terms of π, the area of a sector that intercepts a 40° arc of a circle with a radius of 4.5.

06 2017 26

6 In the diagram below of circle O, chord $\overline{DF}$ bisects chord $\overline{BC}$ at E.

06 2017 08

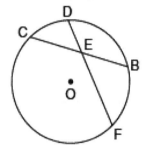

If $BC = 12$ and FE is 5 more than DE, then FE is

1)   13   2)   9

3)   6   4)   4

7 In the diagram below, $m\overset{\frown}{ABC} = 268°$.

06 2017 04

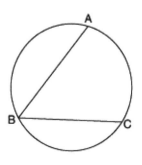

What is the number of degrees in the measure of $\angle ABC$?

1) 134º
2) 92º
3) 68º
4) 46º

8   In circle O, diameter $\overline{AB}$, chord $\overline{BC}$, and radius $\overline{OC}$ are drawn, and the measure of arc BC is 108°.

08 2016 19

Some students wrote these formulas to find the area of sector COB:

Amy $\dfrac{3}{10} \cdot \pi \cdot (BC)^2$

Beth $\dfrac{108}{360} \cdot \pi \cdot (OC)^2$

Carl $\dfrac{3}{10} \cdot \pi \cdot (\frac{1}{2} AB)^2$

Dex $\dfrac{108}{360} \cdot \pi \cdot \frac{1}{2} (AB)^2$

Which students wrote correct formulas?

1) Amy and Dex
2) Beth and Carl
3) Carl and Amy
4) Dex and Beth

9   In the diagram below, $\overline{BC}$ is the
     diameter of circle *A*.

08 2016 23

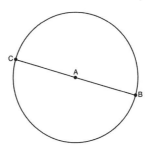

Point *D*, which is unique from points *B* and *C*, is plotted on
circle *A*. Which statement must always be true?

1) $\triangle BCD$ is a right triangle.
2) $\triangle BCD$ is an isosceles triangle.
3) $\triangle BAD$ and $\triangle CBD$ are similar triangles.
4) $\triangle BAD$ and $\triangle CAD$ are congruent triangles.

10 Lines *AE* and *BD* are tangent to circles *O* and *P* at *A*, *E*, *B*, and *D*, as shown in the diagram below. If $AC:CE = 5:3$, and $BD = 56$, determine and state the length of $\overline{CD}$.

08 2016 25

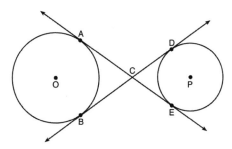

11 Given: Circle *O*, chords $\overline{AB}$ and $\overline{CD}$ intersect at *E*

08 2016 35

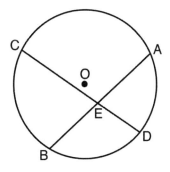

Theorem: If two chords intersect in a circle, the product of the lengths of the segments of one chord is equal to the product of the lengths of the segments of the other chord. Prove this theorem by proving $AE \cdot EB = CE \cdot ED$.

12 In the diagram below of circle O,
    $\overline{OB}$ and $\overline{OC}$ are radii, and chords
    $\overline{AB}$, $\overline{BC}$, and $\overline{AC}$ are drawn.

06 2016 10

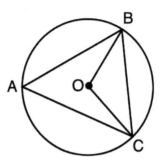

Which statement must always be true?

1) $\angle BAC \cong \angle BOC$
2) $m\angle BAC = \dfrac{1}{2} m\angle BOC$
3) $\triangle BAC$ and $\triangle BOC$ are isosceles.
4) The area of $\triangle BAC$ is twice the area of
    $\triangle BOC$.

13   What is the area of a sector of a circle
      with a radius of 8 inches and formed by
      a central angle that measures 60°?

06 2016 24

1) $\dfrac{8\pi}{3}$

2) $\dfrac{16\pi}{3}$

3) $\dfrac{32\pi}{3}$

4) $\dfrac{64\pi}{3}$

14   In the diagram below, Circle 1 has
      radius 4, while Circle 2 has radius 6.5.
      Angle A intercepts an arc of length π, and
      angle B intercepts an arc of length $\dfrac{13\pi}{8}$.

06 2016 29

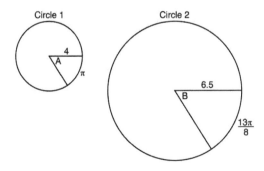

Dominic thinks that angles A and B have the same radian
measure. State whether Dominic is correct or not.
Explain why.

15   What are the coordinates of the center
      and length of the radius of the circle
      whose equation is
      $x^2 + 6x + y^2 - 4y = 23$?

01 2016 17

1) $(3,-2)$ and 36
2) $(3,-2)$ and 6
3) $(-3,2)$ and 36
4) $(-3,2)$ and 6

16   In the diagram below of circle O with
      diameter $\overline{BC}$ and radius $\overline{OA}$, chord
      $\overline{DC}$ is parallel to chord $\overline{BA}$.

01 2016 26

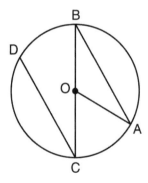

If $m\angle BCD = 30°$, determine and state $m\angle AOB$.

17   Linda is designing a circular piece of
      stained glass with a diameter of 7 inches.
      She is going to sketch a square inside the
      circular region. To the *nearest tenth of
      an inch*, the largest possible length of a side
      of the square is

         1) 3.5
         2) 4.9
         3) 5.0
         4) 6.9

18   In the diagram shown below, $\overline{AC}$
      is tangent to circle O at A and to circle
      P at C, $\overline{OP}$ intersects $\overline{AC}$ at B, $OA = 4$,
      $AB = 5$, and $PC = 10$.

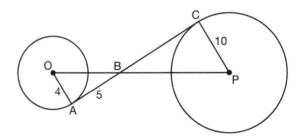

      What is the length of $\overline{BC}$?

      1)   6.4   2)   8

      3)   12.5   4)   16

19   In the diagram below, quadrilateral
      ABCD is inscribed in circle P.

08 2015 15

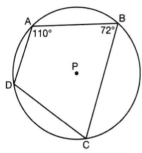

What is m∠ADC?

1)   70°   2)   72°

3)   108°   4)   110°

20   Triangle FGH is inscribed in circle O,
      the length of radius $\overline{OH}$ is 6, and $\overline{FH} \cong \overline{OG}$.

08 2015 18

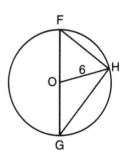

What is the area of the sector formed by angle FOH?

1) 2π 2) $\frac{3}{2}\pi$

3) 6π 4) 24π

21   In the diagram of circle *A* shown below,   06 2015 08
     chords $\overline{CD}$ and $\overline{EF}$ intersect at *G*, and
     chords $\overline{CE}$ and $\overline{FD}$ are drawn.

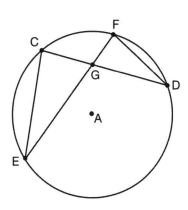

Which statement is *not* always true?

1) $\overline{CG} \cong \overline{FG}$

2) $\angle CEG \cong \angle FDG$

3) $\dfrac{CE}{EG} = \dfrac{FD}{DG}$

4) $\triangle CEG \sim \triangle FDG$

22 In circle *O* shown below, diameter
$\overline{AC}$ is perpendicular to $\overline{CD}$ at point *C*,
and chords $\overline{AB}$, $\overline{BC}$, $\overline{AE}$, and $\overline{CE}$ are drawn.

06 2015 20

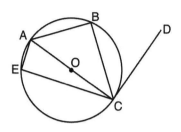

Which statement is *not* always true?

1) $\angle ACB \cong \angle BCD$
2) $\angle ABC \cong \angle ACD$
3) $\angle BAC \cong \angle DCB$
4) $\angle CBA \cong \angle AEC$

23 In the diagram below of circle *O*,
the area of the shaded sector *AOC* is $12\pi \text{ in}^2$
and the length of $\overline{OA}$ is 6 inches.
Determine and state m$\angle AOC$.

06 2015 29

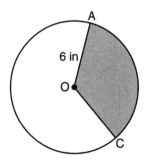

6 in

Similarity

1 Kirstie is testing values that would make triangle *KLM* a right triangle when $\overline{LN}$ is an altitude, and *KM* = 16, as shown below.

08 2017 18

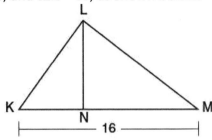

Which lengths would make triangle *KLM* a right triangle?

1) *LM* = 13 and *KN* = 6   3) *KL* = 11 and *KN* = 7

2) *LM* = 12 and *NM* = 9   4) *LN* = 8 and *NM* = 10

2 In the diagram below of $\triangle ABC$, *D*, *E*, and *F* are the midpoints of $\overline{AB}$, $\overline{BC}$, and $\overline{CA}$, respectively.

08 2017 16

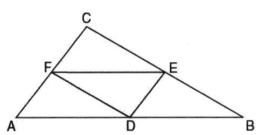

What is the ratio of the area of $\triangle CFE$ to the area of $\triangle CAB$?

1) 1:1   3) 1:3

2) 1:2   4) 1:4

3 In the diagram below, $\angle GRS \cong \angle ART$,   08 2017 09
   $GR = 36$, $SR = 45$, $AR = 15$, and $RT = 18$.

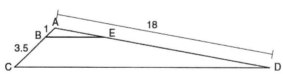

Which triangle similarity statement is correct?

1) $\triangle GRS \sim \triangle ART$ by AA.   3) $\triangle GRS \sim \triangle ART$ by SSS.

2) $\triangle GRS \sim \triangle ART$ by SAS.   4) $\triangle GRS$ is not similar to
$\triangle ART$.

4 In the diagram below, triangle ACD has   08 2017 07
   points B and E on sides $\overline{AC}$ and $\overline{AD}$,
   respectively, such that $\overline{BE} \parallel \overline{CD}$, $AB = 1$,
   $BC = 3.5$, and $AD = 18$.

What is the length of $\overline{AE}$, to the *nearest tenth*?

1) 14.0   3) 3.3

2) 5.1   4) 4.0

5 In the diagram below, $\overline{AD}$ intersects
   $\overline{BE}$ at C, and $\overline{AB} \| \overline{DE}$

08 2017 05

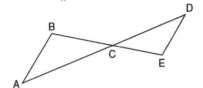

If CD = 6.6 cm, DE = 3.4 cm, CE = 4.2 cm, and BC = 5.25
cm, what is the length of $\overline{AC}$, to the *nearest hundredth of
a centimeter?*

1) 2.70   3) 5.28
2) 3.34   4) 8.25

6 In right triangle *ABC* shown below, altitude
   $\overline{CD}$ is drawn to hypotenuse $\overline{AB}$.
   Explain why $\triangle ABC \sim \triangle ACD$.

06 2017 29

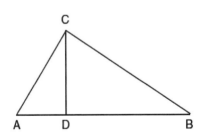

7 In the diagram below, $AC = 7.2$ and $CE = 2.4$.

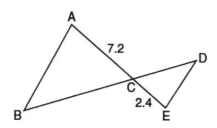

Which statement is *not* sufficient to prove
$\triangle ABC \sim \triangle EDC$?

1) $\overline{AB} \parallel \overline{ED}$
2) $DE = 2.7$ and $AB = 8.1$
3) $CD = 3.6$ and $BC = 10.8$
4) $DE = 3.0$, $AB = 9.0$, $CD = 2.9$, and $BC = 8.7$

8 Given $\triangle MRO$ shown below, with
   trapezoid *PTRO*, $MR = 9$, $MP = 2$,
   and $PO = 4$.

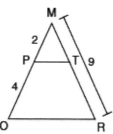

What is the length of $\overline{TR}$?

1)   4.5   2)   5

3)   3   4)   6

80

9   In the diagram of right triangle *ABC*,
    $\overline{CD}$ intersects hypotenuse $\overline{AB}$ at *D*.

08 2016 10

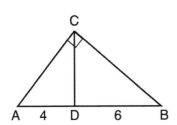

If *AD* = 4 and *DB* = 6, which length of $\overline{AC}$ makes
$\overline{CD} \perp \overline{AB}$?

1) $2\sqrt{6}$ 2) $2\sqrt{10}$

3) $2\sqrt{15}$ 4) $4\sqrt{2}$

10   In triangle *CHR*, *O* is on $\overline{HR}$, and *D*
     is on $\overline{CR}$ so that $\angle H \cong RDO$.

08 2016 12

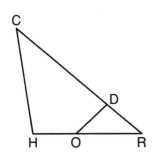

If *RD* = 4, *RO* = 6, and *OH* = 4, what is the length of $\overline{CD}$?

1) $2\dfrac{2}{3}$ 2) $6\dfrac{2}{3}$

3)   11   4)   15

11 Given: △*ABE* and △*CBD* shown in
the diagram below with $\overline{DB} \cong \overline{BE}$

08 2016 22

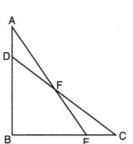

Which statement is needed to prove △*ABE* ≅ △*CBD*
using only SAS ≅ SAS?

1) ∠*CDB* ≅ ∠*AEB*
2) ∠*AFD* ≅ ∠*EFC*
3) $\overline{AD} \cong \overline{CE}$
4) $\overline{AE} \cong \overline{CD}$

12 A three-inch line segment is dilated
by a scale factor of 6 and centered
at its midpoint.
What is the length of its image?

06 2016 02

1) 9 inches 2) 2 inches

3) 15 inches 4) 18 inches

13 Using the information given below,
which set of triangles can *not* be
proven similar?

06 2016 05

1)

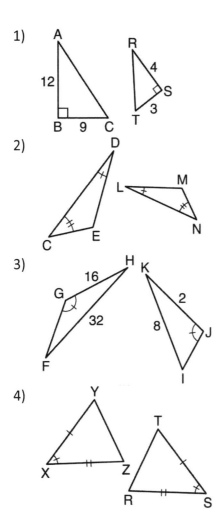

2)

3)

4)

14 In the diagram below, $\overline{DB}$ and $\overline{AF}$ intersect at point C, and $\overline{AD}$ and $\overline{FBE}$ are drawn.

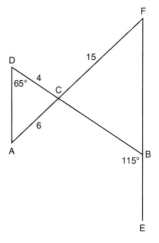

If $AC = 6$, $DC = 4$, $FC = 15$, $m\angle D = 65°$, and $m\angle CBE = 115°$, what is the length of $\overline{CB}$?

1)   10   2)   12

3)   17   4)   22.5

15 In the diagram of $\triangle ABC$, points D and E are on $\overline{AB}$ and $\overline{CB}$, respectively, such that $\overline{AC} \parallel \overline{DE}$.

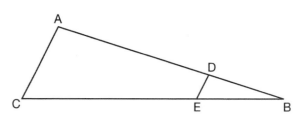

If $AD = 24$, $DB = 12$, and $DE = 4$, what is the length of $\overline{AC}$?

1)   8   2)   12
3)   16   4)   72

16   In $\triangle CED$ as shown below, points A and B   06 2016 27
are located on sides $\overline{CE}$ and $\overline{ED}$,
respectively. Line segment AB is drawn
such that $AE = 3.75$, $AC = 5$, $EB = 4.5$,
and $BD = 6$.

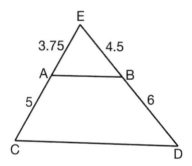

Explain why $\overline{AB}$ is parallel to $\overline{CD}$.

17   In the diagram below, $\triangle ABC \sim \triangle DEF$.   01 2016 13

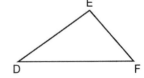

If $AB = 6$ and $AC = 8$, which statement will justify
similarity by SAS?

85

1) $DE = 9$, $DF = 12$, and $\angle A \cong \angle D$
2) $DE = 8$, $DF = 10$, and $\angle A \cong \angle D$
3) $DE = 36$, $DF = 64$, and $\angle C \cong \angle F$
4) $DE = 15$, $DF = 20$, and $\angle C \cong \angle F$

18   The aspect ratio (the ratio of screen width to height) of a rectangular flat-screen television is $16:9$. The length of the diagonal of the screen is the television's screen size. Determine and state, to the *nearest inch*, the screen size (diagonal) of this flat-screen television with a screen height of 20.6 inches.

01 2016 32

19   In the diagram shown below, $\overline{AC}$ is tangent to circle O at A and to circle P at C, $\overline{OP}$ intersects $\overline{AC}$ at B, OA = 4, AB = 5, and PC = 10.

08 2015 12

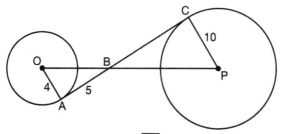

What is the length of $\overline{BC}$?

1) 6.4
2) 8
3) 12.5
4) 16

20 In the diagram below, $\triangle DEF$ is the image of $\triangle ABC$ after a clockwise rotation of 180° and a dilation where $AB = 3$, $BC = 5.5$, $AC = 4.5$, $DE = 6$, $FD = 9$, and $EF = 11$.

08 2015 14

Which relationship must always be true?

1) $\dfrac{m\angle A}{m\angle D} = \dfrac{1}{2}$

2) $\dfrac{m\angle C}{m\angle F} = \dfrac{2}{1}$

3) $\dfrac{m\angle A}{m\angle C} = \dfrac{m\angle F}{m\angle D}$

4) $\dfrac{m\angle B}{m\angle E} = \dfrac{m\angle C}{m\angle F}$

21 In the diagram below, $\triangle ABC \sim \triangle ADE$.

08 2015 17

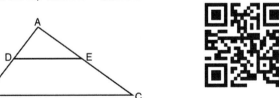

Which measurements are justified by this similarity?

1) $AD = 3$, $AB = 6$, $AE = 4$, and $AC = 12$
2) $AD = 5$, $AB = 8$, $AE = 7$, and $AC = 10$
3) $AD = 3$, $AB = 9$, $AE = 5$, and $AC = 10$
4) $AD = 2$, $AB = 6$, $AE = 5$, and $AC = 15$

22   As shown in the diagram below, $\overline{AB}$ and
      $\overline{CD}$ intersect at E, and $\overline{AC} \parallel \overline{BD}$.

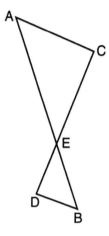

Given $\triangle AEC \sim \triangle BED$, which equation is true?

1) $\dfrac{CE}{DE} = \dfrac{EB}{EA}$

2) $\dfrac{AE}{BE} = \dfrac{AC}{BD}$

3) $\dfrac{EC}{AE} = \dfrac{BE}{ED}$

4) $\dfrac{ED}{EC} = \dfrac{AC}{BD}$

23   To find the distance across a pond   08 2015 27
      from point *B* to point *C*, a surveyor
      drew the diagram below. The measurements
      he made are indicated on his diagram.

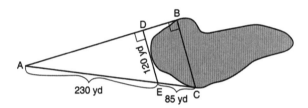

Use the surveyor's information to determine and state
the distance from point *B* to point *C*, to the *nearest yard*.

24   Triangles *RST* and *XYZ* are drawn below.   08 2015 29
      If $RS = 6$, $ST = 14$, $XY = 9$, $YZ = 21$,
      and $\angle S \cong \angle Y$, is $\triangle RST$ similar to $\triangle XYZ$?
      Justify your answer.

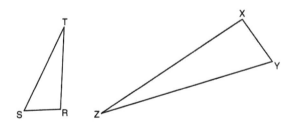

25   In the diagram of $\triangle ADC$ below, $\overline{EB} \parallel \overline{DC}$, $AE = 9$, $ED = 5$, and $AB = 9.2$.

06 2015 11

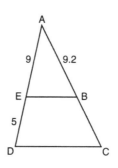

What is the length of $\overline{AC}$, to the *nearest tenth*?

1)   5.1   2)   5.2

3)   14.3   4)   14.4

26   Triangles *ABC* and *DEF* are drawn below.

06 2015 15

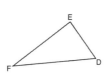

If $AB = 9$, $BC = 15$, $DE = 6$, $EF = 10$, and $\angle B \cong \angle E$, which statement is true?

1) $\angle CAB \cong \angle DEF$ 2) $\dfrac{AB}{CB} = \dfrac{FE}{DE}$

3) $\triangle ABC \sim \triangle DEF$ 4) $\dfrac{AB}{DE} = \dfrac{FE}{CB}$

27   In the diagram below, $\triangle ABC \sim \triangle DEC$.

06 2015 21

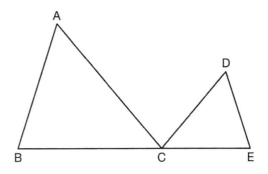

If $AC = 12$, $DC = 7$, $DE = 5$, and the perimeter of $\triangle ABC$ is 30, what is the perimeter of $\triangle DEC$?

1) 12.5
2) 14.0
3) 14.8
4) 17.5

28   A flagpole casts a shadow 16.60 meters long. Tim stands at a distance of 12.45 meters from the base of the flagpole, such that the end of Tim's shadow meets the end of the flagpole's shadow. If Tim is 1.65 meters tall, determine and state the height of the flagpole to the *nearest tenth of a meter.*

06 2015 31

29   In the diagram below, the line of sight
      from the park ranger station, *P*, to the
      lifeguard chair, *L*, on the beach of a lake is
      perpendicular to the path joining the
      campground, *C*, and the first aid station, *F*.
      The campground is 0.25 mile from the
      lifeguard chair. The straight paths from
      both the campground and first aid station
      to the park ranger station are perpendicular.

06 2015 34

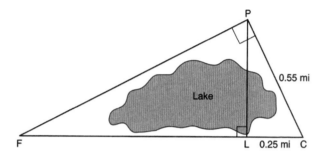

If the path from the park ranger station to the
campground is 0.55 mile, determine and state, to the
nearest hundredth of a mile, the distance between the
park ranger station and the lifeguard chair.

Gerald believes the distance from the first aid station to
the campground is at least 1.5 miles. Is Gerald correct?
Justify your answer.

Trigonometry

1 In a right triangle, $\sin(40-x)° = \cos(3x)°$.
   What is the value of x?

   08 2017 21

   1) 10   3) 20

   2) 15   4) 25

2 In right triangle ABC, $m\angle A = 32°$,
   $m\angle B = 90°$, and $AC = 6.2$ cm. What
   is the length of $\overline{BC}$, to the *nearest
   tenth of a centimeter*?

   08 2017 19

   1) 3.3   3) 5.3

   2) 3.9   4) 11.7

3 To build a handicapped-access ramp,
   the building code states that for every
   1 inch of vertical rise in height, the
   ramp must extend out 12 inches
   horizontally, as shown in the diagram
   below.

   08 2017 15

   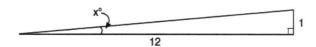

   What is the angle of inclination, *x*, of this ramp, to the
   nearest hundredth of a degree?

   1) 4.76   3) 85.22

   2) 4.78   4) 85.24

4 Freda, who is training to use a radar system, detects an airplane flying at a constant speed and heading in a straight line to pass directly over her location. She sees the airplane at an angle of elevation of 15° and notes that it is maintaining a constant altitude of 6250 feet. One minute later, she sees the airplane at an angle of elevation of 52°. How far has the airplane traveled, to the *nearest foot*? Determine and state the speed of the airplane, to the *nearest mile per hour*.

06 2017 36

5 A ladder 20 feet long leans against a building, forming an angle of 71° with the level ground. To the *nearest foot*, how high up the wall of the building does the ladder touch the building?

06 2017 21

1) 15   2) 16

3) 18   4) 19

6 In the diagram of $\triangle RST$ below, $m\angle T = 90°$, $RS = 65$, and $ST = 60$.

06 2017 13

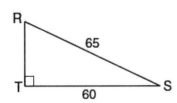

What is the measure of $\angle S$, to the *nearest degree*?

1) 23º   2) 43º

3) 47º   4) 67º

7 In right triangle *ABC*, $m\angle C = 90°$. If $\cos B = \dfrac{5}{13}$, which function also equals $\dfrac{5}{13}$?

1)　　　$\tan A$　　　　　　2)　　　$\tan B$

3)　　　$\sin A$　　　　　　4)　　　$\sin B$

8 In $\triangle ABC$, where $\angle C$ is a right angle, $\cos A = \dfrac{\sqrt{21}}{5}$. What is $\sin B$?

1)　　$\dfrac{\sqrt{21}}{5}$　　　　　　2)　　$\dfrac{\sqrt{21}}{2}$

3)　　$\dfrac{2}{5}$　　　　　　4)　　$\dfrac{5}{\sqrt{21}}$

9 In the diagram below, a window of a house is 15 feet above the ground. A ladder is placed against the house with its base at an angle of 75° with the ground. Determine and state the length of the ladder to the *nearest tenth of a foot.*

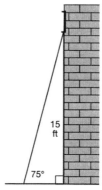

15 ft

75°

10 As modeled below, a movie is projected onto a large outdoor screen. The bottom of the 60-foot-tall screen is 12 feet off the ground. The projector sits on the ground at a horizontal distance of 75 feet from the screen.

08 2016 34

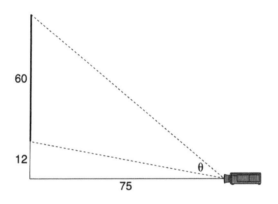

Determine and state, to the *nearest tenth of a degree*, the measure of θ, the projection angle.

11 A 20-foot support post leans against a wall, making a 70° angle with the ground. To the *nearest tenth of a foot*, how far up the wall will the support post reach?

06 2016 11

1) 6.8
2) 6.9
3) 18.7
4) 18.8

12 In the diagram below, $\triangle ERM \sim \triangle JTM$.

06 2016 15

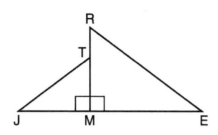

Which statement is always true?

1) $\cos J = \dfrac{RM}{RE}$

2) $\cos R = \dfrac{JM}{JT}$

3) $\tan T = \dfrac{RM}{EM}$

4) $\tan E = \dfrac{TM}{JM}$

13 Find the value of R that will make
the equation $\sin 73° = \cos R$ true
when $0° < R < 90°$.
Explain your answer.

06 2016 28

14   A ladder leans against a building. The top of
the ladder touches the building 10 feet above
the ground. The foot of the ladder is 4 feet
from the building. Find, to the *nearest degree*,
the angle that the ladder makes with the
level ground.

06 2016 30

15 In $\triangle ABC$, the complement of $\angle B$ is $\angle A$
Which statement is always true?

1) $\tan \angle A = \tan \angle B$
2) $\sin \angle A = \sin \angle B$
3) $\cos \angle A = \tan \angle B$
4) $\sin \angle A = \cos \angle B$

16 In the diagram below of circle O, the area
of the shaded sector LOM is $2\pi \ \mathrm{cm}^2$.

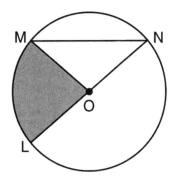

If the length of $\overline{NL}$ is 6 cm, what is m$\angle$N ?

1) 10°
2) 20°
3) 40°
4) 80°

17 In the diagram of right triangle *ABC* shown below, *AB* = 14 and *AC* = 9.

01 2016 16

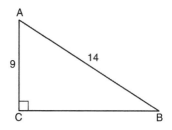

What is the measure of ∠*A*, to the *nearest degree*?

1) 33
2) 40
3) 50
4) 57

18 A carpenter leans an extension ladder against a house to reach the bottom of a window 30 feet above the ground. As shown in the diagram below, the ladder makes a 70° angle with the ground. To the *nearest foot*, determine and state the length of the ladder.

01 2016 29

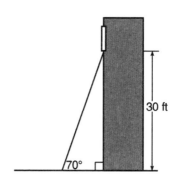

19   Cathy wants to determine the height
of the flagpole shown in the diagram
below. She uses a survey instrument to
measure the angle of elevation to the top
of the flagpole, and determines it to be 34.9°.
She walks 8 meters closer and determines
the new measure of the angle of elevation
to be 52.8°. At each measurement, the
survey instrument is 1.7 meters above the ground.

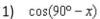

52.8°   34.9°   1.7 m

8 m

Determine and state, to the *nearest tenth of a meter*,
the height of the flagpole.

20   Which expression is always equivalent
to $\sin x$ when $0° < x < 90°$?

1) $\cos(90° - x)$
2) $\cos(45° - x)$
3) $\cos(2x)$
4) $\cos x$

100

21   As shown in the diagram below, a ship
      is heading directly toward a lighthouse
      whose beacon is 125 feet above sea level.
      At the first sighting, point A, the angle of
      elevation from the ship to the light was 7°.
      A short time later, at point D, the angle
      of elevation was 16°.

08 2015 32

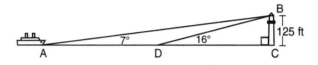

To the *nearest foot*, determine and state how far the ship
traveled from point A to point D.

22   As shown in the diagram below, the
      angle of elevation from a point on the
      ground to the top of the tree is 34°.

06 2015 05

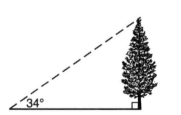

If the point is 20 feet from the base of the tree, what is
the height of the tree, to the *nearest tenth of a foot*?

    1) 29.7
    2) 16.6
    3) 13.5
    4) 11.2

23   In scalene triangle *ABC* shown in the
      diagram below, m∠*C* = 90°.

06 2015 12

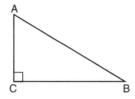

Which equation is always true?

    1) $\sin A = \sin B$
    2) $\cos A = \cos B$
    3) $\cos A = \sin C$
    4) $\sin A = \cos B$

24   The diagram below shows a ramp
      connecting the ground to a loading
      platform 4.5 feet above the ground.
      The ramp measures 11.75 feet from
      the ground to the top of the loading platform.

06 2015 28

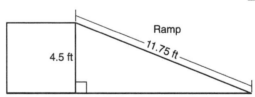

Determine and state, to the *nearest degree*, the angle of
elevation formed by the ramp and the ground.

25   A flagpole casts a shadow 16.60 meters long. Tim stands at a distance of 12.45 meters from the base of the flagpole, such that the end of Tim's shadow meets the end of the flagpole's shadow. If Tim is 1.65 meters tall, determine and state the height of the flagpole to the *nearest tenth of a meter.*

06 2015 31

Parallelograms and Trapezoids

1 Isosceles trapezoid *ABCD* has bases
   $\overline{DC}$ and $\overline{AB}$ with nonparallel legs
   $\overline{AD}$ and $\overline{BC}$. Segments *AE, BE, CE*,
   and *DE* are drawn in trapezoid
   ABCD such that $\angle CDE \cong \angle DCE$,
   $\overline{AE} \perp \overline{DE}$, and $\overline{BE} \perp \overline{CE}$.

08 2017 35

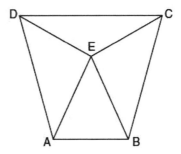

Prove $\triangle ADE \cong \triangle BCE$ and prove $\triangle AEB$ is an isosceles
triangle.

2 In the diagram of rhombus *PQRS* below,
   the diagonals $\overline{PR}$ and $\overline{QS}$ intersect at
   point *T*, $PR = 16$, and $QS = 30$.
   Determine and state the perimeter of *PQRS*.

08 2017 26

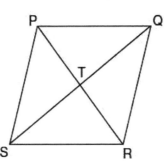

3   If *ABCD* is a parallelogram, which statement
would prove that *ABCD* is a rhombus?

08 2017 14

1) $\angle ABC \cong \angle CDA$ 3) $\overline{AC} \perp \overline{BD}$

2) $\overline{AC} \cong \overline{BD}$ 4) $\overline{AB} \perp \overline{CD}$

4   In the diagram below of parallelogram
ROCK, m$\angle C$ is 70° and m$\angle ROS$ is 65°.

08 2017 08

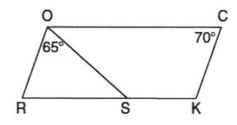

What is m$\angle KSO$?

1) 45º   3) 115º

2) 110º   4) 135º

5   In quadrilateral *BLUE* shown below,
    $\overline{BE} \cong \overline{UL}$.

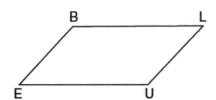

Which information would be sufficient to prove
quadrilateral *BLUE* is a parallelogram?

1) $\overline{BL} \parallel \overline{EU}$
2) $\overline{LU} \parallel \overline{BE}$
3) $\overline{BE} \cong \overline{BL}$
4) $\overline{LU} \cong \overline{EU}$

6   Which set of statements would describe
    a parallelogram that can always be
    classified as a rhombus?

I.   Diagonals are perpendicular
     bisectors of each other.
II. Diagonals bisect the angles from
     which they are drawn.
III. Diagonals form four congruent isosceles right
     triangles.

1) I and II
2) I and III
3) II and III
4) I, II, and III

7   Quadrilateral *ABCD* with diagonals $\overline{AC}$
    and $\overline{BD}$ is shown in the diagram below.

08 2016 07

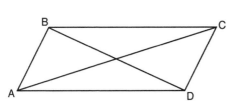

Which information is *not* enough to prove *ABCD*
is a parallelogram?

1) $\overline{AB} \cong \overline{CD}$ and $\overline{AB} \parallel \overline{DC}$
2) $\overline{AB} \cong \overline{CD}$ and $\overline{BC} \cong \overline{DA}$
3) $\overline{AB} \cong \overline{CD}$ and $\overline{BC} \parallel \overline{AD}$
4) $\overline{AB} \parallel \overline{DC}$ and $\overline{BC} \parallel \overline{AD}$

8   In the diagram below, *ABCD* is a
    parallelogram, $\overline{AB}$ is extended through
    B to *E*, and $\overline{CE}$ is drawn.

08 2016 24

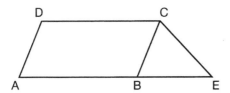

If $\overline{CE} \cong \overline{BE}$ and $m\angle D = 112°$, what is $m\angle E$?

1)   44°   2)   56°

3)   68°   4)   112°

9 In parallelogram *ABCD*, diagonals $\overline{AC}$
   and $\overline{BD}$ intersect at *E*. Which statement
   does *not* prove parallelogram *ABCD* is a
   rhombus?

06 2016 09

1) $\overline{AC} \cong \overline{DB}$
2) $\overline{AB} \cong \overline{BC}$
3) $\overline{AC} \perp \overline{DB}$
4) $\overline{AC}$ bisects ∠*DCB*

10 Given: Parallelogram *ABCD*, $\overline{EFG}$, and
    diagonal $\overline{DFB}$

06 2016 33

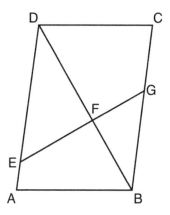

Prove: △*DEF* ~ △*BGF*

108

11 In parallelogram *QRST* shown below, diagonal $\overline{TR}$ is drawn, *U* and *V* are points on $\overline{TS}$ and $\overline{QR}$, respectively, and $\overline{UV}$ intersects $\overline{TR}$ at *W*.

01 2016 03

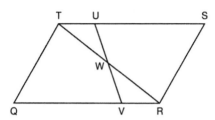

If $m\angle S = 60°$, $m\angle SRT = 83°$, and $m\angle TWU = 35°$, what is $m\angle WVQ$?

1) 37º
2) 60º
3) 72º
4) 83º

12 Given: Parallelogram *ANDR* with $\overline{AW}$ and $\overline{DE}$ bisecting $\overline{NWD}$ and $\overline{REA}$ at points *W* and *E*, respectively

01 2016 35

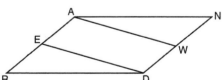

Prove that $\triangle ANW \cong \triangle DRE$. Prove that quadrilateral *AWDE* is a parallelogram.

13 A parallelogram must be a rectangle when its

08 2015 01

1) diagonals are perpendicular
2) diagonals are congruent
3) opposite sides are parallel
4) opposite sides are congruent

14 In the diagram of parallelogram *FRED* shown below, $\overline{ED}$ is extended to *A*, and $\overline{AF}$ is drawn such that $\overline{AF} \cong \overline{DF}$.

08 2015 08

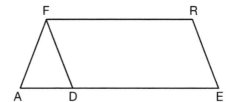

If $m\angle R = 124°$, what is $m\angle AFD$?

1) 124°
2) 112°
3) 68°
4) 56°

15 In parallelogram *ABCD* shown below, diagonals $\overline{AC}$ and $\overline{BD}$ intersect at *E*.

08 2015 28

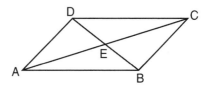

Prove: $\angle ACD \cong \angle CAB$

16   In the diagram of parallelogram
     $ABCD$ below, $\overline{BE} \perp \overline{CED}$, $\overline{DF} \perp \overline{BFC}$,
     $\overline{CE} \cong \overline{CF}$.

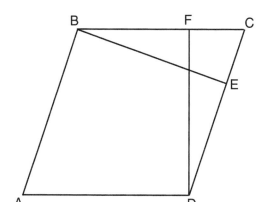

Prove $ABCD$ is a rhombus

17   Quadrilateral $ABCD$ has diagonals
     $\overline{AC}$ and $\overline{BD}$. Which information is
     not sufficient to prove $ABCD$ is a parallelogram?

1) $\overline{AC}$ and $\overline{BD}$ bisect each other.
2) $\overline{AB} \cong \overline{CD}$ and $\overline{BC} \cong \overline{AD}$
3) $\overline{AB} \cong \overline{CD}$ and $\overline{AB} \parallel \overline{CD}$
4) $\overline{AB} \cong \overline{CD}$ and $\overline{BC} \parallel \overline{AD}$

18   The diagram below shows parallelogram
      LMNO with diagonal $\overline{LN}$, m∠*M* = 118°,
      and m∠*LNO* = 22°.

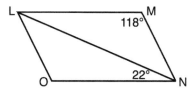

Explain why m∠*NLO* is 40 degrees.

19   Given: Quadrilateral *ABCD* is a
      parallelogram with diagonals
      $\overline{AC}$ and $\overline{BD}$ intersecting at *E*

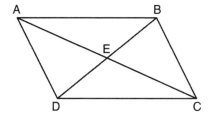

Prove: Δ*AED* ≅ Δ*CEB*

Describe a single rigid motion that maps Δ*AED*
onto Δ*CEB*.

<u>Coordinate Geometry Proofs</u>

1   Triangle *PQR* has vertices $P(-3,-1)$, $Q(-1,7)$, and $R(3,3)$, and points *A* and *B* are midpoints of $\overline{PQ}$ and $\overline{RQ}$, respectively. Use coordinate geometry to prove that $\overline{AB}$ is parallel to $\overline{PR}$ and is half the length of $\overline{PR}$.
[The use of the set of axes below is optional.]

08 2017 32

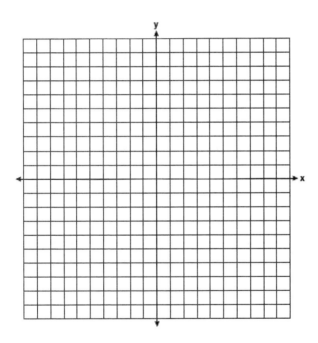

2 In the diagram below of $\triangle ABC$ and $\triangle XYZ$, a sequence of rigid motions maps $\angle A$ onto $\angle X$, $\angle C$ onto $\angle Z$, and $\overline{AC}$ onto $\overline{XZ}$.

08 2017 30

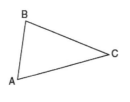

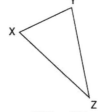

Determine and state whether $\overline{BC} \cong \overline{YZ}$. Explain why.

3 Quadrilateral *PQRS* has vertices $P(-2, 3)$, $Q(3, 8)$, $R(4, 1)$, and $S(-1, -4)$.
Prove that *PQRS* is a rhombus.
Prove that *PQRS* is *not* a square.
[The use of the set of axes below is optional.]

06 2017 35

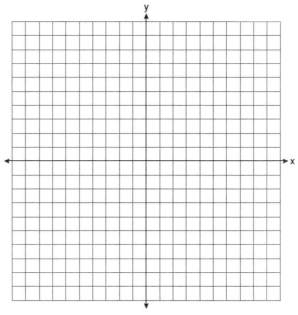

114

4 The grid below shows $\triangle ABC$
   and $\triangle DEF$.

08 2016 33b

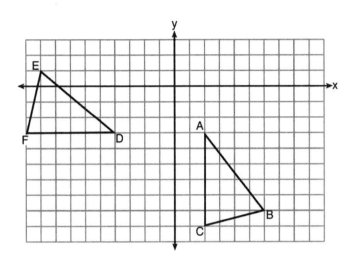

Let $\triangle A'B'C'$ be the image of $\triangle ABC$ after a rotation about point A. Determine and state the location of B' if the location of point C' is $(8,-3)$. Explain your answer. Is $\triangle DEF$ congruent to $\triangle A'B'C'$? Explain your answer.

5   In the diagram below, $\overline{DC}$, $\overline{AC}$, $\overline{DOB}$,

01 2016 21

$\overline{CB}$, and $\overline{AB}$ are chords of circle O, $\overleftrightarrow{FDE}$
is tangent at point D, and radius $\overline{AO}$ is drawn.
Sam decides to apply this theorem to the
diagram: "An angle inscribed in a semi-circle
is a right angle."

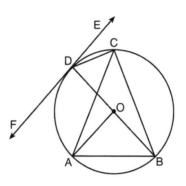

Which angle is Sam referring to?

1) $\angle AOB$
2) $\angle BAC$
3) $\angle DCB$
4) $\angle FDB$

6   A quadrilateral has vertices with
coordinates $(-3, 1)$, $(0, 3)$, $(5, 2)$, and $(-1, -2)$.
Which type of quadrilateral is this?

08 2015 22

1) rhombus
2) rectangle
3) square
4) trapezoid

7   Triangle *ABC* has vertices with $A(x, 3)$,
    $B(-3, -1)$, and $C(-1, -4)$.
    Determine and state a value of x that
    would make triangle ABC a right triangle.
    Justify why $\triangle ABC$ is a right triangle.
    [The use of the set of axes below is optional.]

08 2015 33

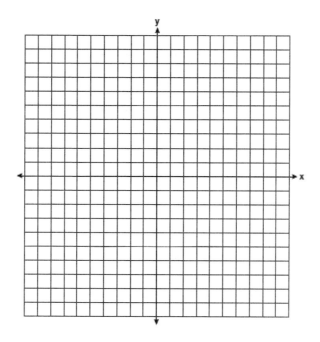

8   In the coordinate plane, the vertices of
     △*RST* are *R*(6,−1), *S*(1,−4), and *T*(−5,6).
     Prove that △*RST* is a right triangle.
     State the coordinates of point *P* such that
     quadrilateral *RSTP* is a rectangle.

06 2015 36

Prove that your quadrilateral *RSTP* is a rectangle.
[The use of the set of axes below is optional.]

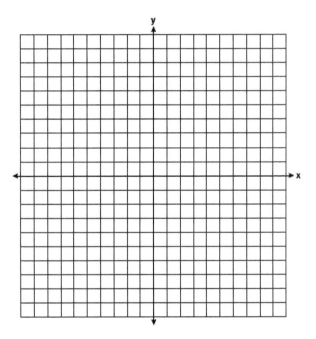

Volume and Solids

1 A rectangular in-ground pool is
modeled by the prism below. The
inside of the pool is 16 feet wide
and 35 feet long. The pool has a
shallow end and a deep end, with
a sloped floor connecting the two ends.

08 2017 36

Without water, the shallow end is 9 feet long and 4.5 feet
deep, and the deep end of the pool is 12.5 feet long.

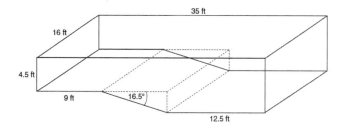

If the sloped floor has an angle of depression of 16.5
degrees, what is the depth of the pool at the deep end, to
the *nearest tenth of a foot*? Find the volume of the inside
of the pool to the *nearest cubic foot*. A garden hose is
used to fill the pool. Water comes out of the hose at a
rate of 10 .5 gallons per minute. How much time, to the
nearest hour, will it take to fill the pool?

2 Sue believes that the two cylinders shown in the diagram below have equal volumes.

08 2017 25

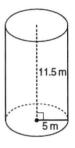

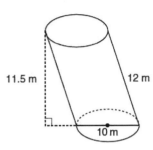

Is Sue correct? Explain why.

3 A rectangle whose length and width are 10 and 6, respectively, is shown below. The rectangle is continuously rotated around a straight line to form an object whose volume is 150π.

08 2017 13

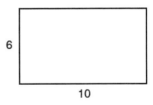

Which line could the rectangle be rotated around?

1) a long side

2) a short side

3) the vertical line of symmetry

4) the horizontal line of symmetry

4   A two-dimensional cross section is taken
    of a three-dimensional object. If this
    cross section is a triangle, what can *not*
    be the three-dimensional object?

08 2017 01

1) cone   3) pyramid
2) cylinder   4) rectangular prism

5   When volleyballs are purchased, they are
    not fully inflated. A partially inflated
    volleyball can be modeled by a sphere
    whose volume is approximately 180 in³.
    After being fully inflated, its volume is
    approximately 294 in³. To the *nearest
    tenth of an inch*, how much does the radius
    increase when the volleyball is fully inflated?

06 2017 28

6   The diagram below shows two figures.
    Figure *A* is a right triangular prism and
    figure *B* is an oblique triangular prism.
    The base of figure *A* has a height of 5 and
    a length of 8 and the height of prism *A* is 14.
    The base of figure *B* has a height of 8 and a
    length of 5 and the height of prism *B* is 14.

06 2017 27

Figure A   **Figure B**

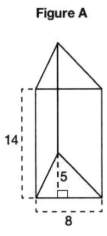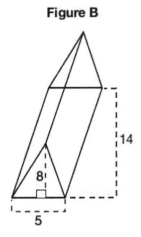

14   14

5   8

8   5

Use Cavalieri's Principle to explain why the volumes of these two triangular prisms are equal.

7   In the diagram below, right triangle *ABC* has legs whose lengths are 4 and 6.

06 2017 18

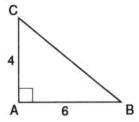

What is the volume of the three-dimensional object formed by continuously rotating the right triangle around $\overline{AB}$?

1)   32π   2)   48π

3)   96π   4)   144π

8 The pyramid shown below has a square base, a height of 7, and a volume of 84.

06 2017 16

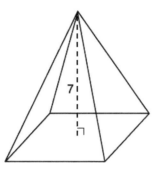

What is the length of the side of the base?

1)   6   2)   12

3)   18   4)   36

9 If an equilateral triangle is continuously rotated around one of its medians, which 3-dimensional object is generated?

08 2016 03

1) cone
2) pyramid
3) prism
4) sphere

10 The cross section of a regular pyramid contains the altitude of the pyramid. The shape of this cross section is a

08 2016 13

1) circle
2) square
3) triangle
4) rectangle

11 Tennis balls are sold in cylindrical cans 08 2016 20
with the balls stacked one on top of the other.
tennis ball has a diameter of 6.7 cm. To the
nearest cubic centimeter, what is the minimum
volume of the can that holds a stack of 4 tennis
balls?

1) 236
2) 282
3) 564
4) 945

12 A student has a rectangular postcard 06 2016 01
that he folds in half lengthwise. Next,
he rotates it continuously about the
folded edge. Which three-dimensional
object below is generated by this rotation?

1)

2)

3)

4)

13 A hemispherical water tank has an inside
diameter of 10 feet. If water has a density
of 62.4 pounds per cubic foot, what is
the weight of the water in a full tank,
to the *nearest pound*?

06 2016 20

1)   16,336   2)   32,673

3)   130,690   4)   261,381

14 A water glass can be modeled by a
truncated right cone (a cone which
is cut parallel to its base) as shown below.

06 2016 36

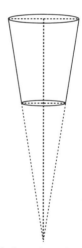

The diameter of the top of the glass is 3 inches, the
diameter at the bottom of the glass is 2 inches, and the
height of the glass is 5 inches. The base with a diameter
of 2 inches must be parallel to the base with a diameter
of 3 inches in order to find the height of the cone. Explain
why. Determine and state, in inches, the height of the
larger cone. Determine and state, to the *nearest tenth of
a cubic inch*, the volume of the water glass.

15   William is drawing pictures of cross
      sections of the right circular cone below.

01 2016 01

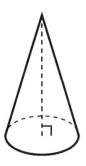

Which drawing can *not* be a cross section of a cone?

1)

2)

3)

4)

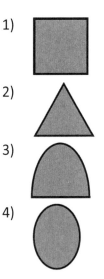

16   As shown in the diagram below, a regular   01 2016 07
pyramid has a square base whose side
measures 6 inches.

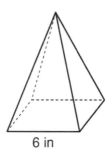

6 in

If the altitude of the pyramid measures 12
inches, its volume, in cubic inches, is

  1) 72
  2) 144
  3) 288
  4) 432

17   The diameter of a basketball is   01 2016 14
approximately 9.5 inches and the diameter
of a tennis ball is approximately 2.5 inches.
The volume of the basketball is about how
many times greater than the volume of the
tennis ball?

  1)   3591   2)   65

  3)   55   4)   4

18 Molly wishes to make a lawn ornament
in the form of a solid sphere. The clay
being used to make the sphere weighs
.075 pound per cubic inch. If the sphere's
radius is 4 inches, what is the weight of the
sphere, to the *nearest pound*?

01 2016 19

1) 34
2) 20
3) 15
4) 4

19 If the rectangle below is continuously
rotated about side *w*, which solid figure
is formed?

08 2015 03

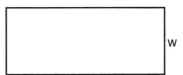

1) pyramid
2) rectangular prism
3) cone
4) cylinder

20   The Great Pyramid of Giza was
      constructed as a regular pyramid with
      a square base. It was built with an
      approximate volume of 2,592,276 cubic
      meters and a height of 146.5 meters.
      What was the length of one side of its base,
      to the *nearest meter*?

08 2015 21

      1) 73
      2) 77
      3) 133
      4) 230

21   Which object is formed when right
      triangle *RST* shown below is rotated
      around leg $\overline{RS}$?

06 2015 01

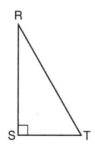

      1) a pyramid with a square base
      2) an isosceles triangle
      3) a right triangle
      4) a cone

22   Which figure can have the same cross section as a sphere?

06 2015 06

1)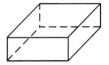

2)

3)

4)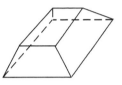

23   A circle with a radius of 5 was divided into 24 congruent sectors. The sectors were then rearranged, as shown in the diagram below.

06 2015 23

To the *nearest integer*, the value of x is

1)   31   2)   16

3)   12   4)   10

Modeling

1   The 2010 U.S. Census populations
    and population densities are shown
    in the table below.

08 2017 20

State	Population Density $\left(\dfrac{people}{mi^2} \right)$	Population in 2010
Florida	350.6	18,801,310
Illinois	231.1	12,830,632
New York	411.2	19,378,102
Pennsylvania	283.9	12,702,379

Based on the table above, which list has the states' areas,
in square miles, in order from largest to smallest?

1) Illinois, Florida, New
   York, Pennsylvania

3) New York, Florida,
   Pennsylvania, Illinois

2) New York, Florida,
   Illinois, Pennsylvania

4) Pennsylvania, New York,
   Florida, Illinois

2 A gas station has a cylindrical fueling tank
   that holds the gasoline for its pumps, as
   modeled below. The tank holds a
   maximum of 20,000 gallons of gasoline
   and has a length of 34.5 feet.

06 2017 34

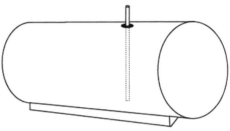

A metal pole is used to measure how much gas is in the
tank. To the *nearest tenth of a foot*, how long does the
pole need to be in order to reach the bottom of the tank
and still extend one foot outside the tank? Justify your
answer. [1 ft³=7.48 gallons]

3 A fabricator is hired to make a 27-foot-
   long solid metal railing for the stairs at the
   local library. The railing is modeled by the
   diagram below. The railing is 2.5 inches high
   and 2.5 inches wide and is comprised of a
   rectangular prism and a half-cylinder.

06 2017 23

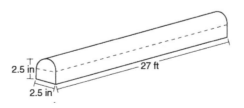

2.5 in

2.5 in

27 ft

How much metal, to the *nearest cubic inch*,
will the railing contain?

1)   151   2)   795

3)   1808   4)   2025

4 The density of the American white oak
   tree is 752 kilograms per cubic meter.
   If the trunk of an American white oak tree
   has a circumference of 4.5 meters and the
   height of the trunk is 8 meters, what is the
   approximate number of kilograms of the trunk?

08 2016 17

1)   13   2)   9694

3)   13,536   4)   30,456

5 A snow cone consists of a paper cone
   completely filled with shaved ice and
   topped with a hemisphere of shaved ice,
   as shown in the diagram below. The inside
   diameter of both the cone and the
   hemisphere is 8.3 centimeters. The height
   of the cone is 10.2 centimeters.

08 2016 36

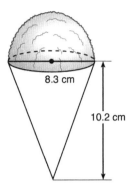

The desired density of the shaved ice is 0.697 g/cm^3, and the cost, per kilogram, of ice is $3.83. Determine and state the cost of the ice needed to make 50 snow cones.

6   Seawater contains approximately 1.2 ounces of salt per liter on average. How many gallons of seawater, to the *nearest tenth of a gallon*, would contain 1 pound of salt?

06 2016 18

1)   3.3
2)   3.5
3)   4.7
4)   13.3

7   A barrel of fuel oil is a right circular cylinder where the inside measurements of the barrel are a diameter of 22.5 inches and a height of 33.5 inches. There are 231 cubic inches in a liquid gallon. Determine and state, to the *nearest tenth*, the gallons of fuel that are in a barrel of fuel oil.

06 2016 32

8   A fish tank in the shape of a rectangular
     prism has dimensions of 14 inches, 16 inches,
     and 10 inches. The tank contains 1680 cubic
     inches of water. What percent of the fish
     tank is empty?

01 2016 04

     1) 10
     2) 25
     3) 50
     4) 75

9   A designer needs to create perfectly
     circular necklaces. The necklaces each
     need to have a radius of 10 cm. What is
     the largest number of necklaces that can
     be made from 1000 cm of wire?

01 2016 23

     1) 15
     2) 16
     3) 31
     4) 32

10   During an experiment, the same type of
     bacteria is grown in two petri dishes.
     Petri dish A has a diameter of 51 mm and has
     approximately 40,000 bacteria after 1 hour.
     Petri dish B has a diameter of 75 mm and
     has approximately 72,000 bacteria after
     1 hour.

01 2016 30

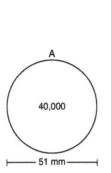

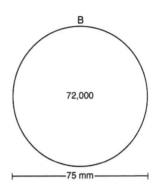

Determine and state which petri dish has the greater population density of bacteria at the end of the first hour.

11 A hemispherical tank is filled with water and has a diameter of 10 feet. If water weighs 62.4 pounds per cubic foot, what is the total weight of the water in a full tank, to the *nearest pound*?

08 2015 16

1) 16,336
2) 32,673
3) 130,690
4) 261,381

12 A wooden cube has an edge length of 6 centimeters and a mass of 137.8 grams. Determine the density of the cube, to the *nearest thousandth*. State which type of wood the cube is made of, using the density table below.

08 2015 25

Type of Wood	Density (g/cm³)
Pine	0.373
Hemlock	0.431
Elm	0.554
Birch	0.601
Ash	0.638
Maple	0.676
Oak	0.711

13   Walter wants to make 100 candles in the
shape of a cone for his new candle business.
The mold shown below will be used to make
the candles. Each mold will have a height of
8 inches and a diameter of 3 inches. To the
nearest cubic inch, what will be the total
volume of 100 candles?

08 2015 36

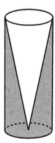

Walter goes to a hobby store to buy the wax for his
candles. The wax costs $0.10 per ounce. If the weight of
the wax is 0.52 ounce per cubic inch, how much will it
cost Walter to buy the wax for 100 candles? If Walter
spent a total of $37.83 for the molds and charges $1.95
for each candle, what is Walter's profit after selling 100
candles?

14   A shipping container is in the shape
of a right rectangular prism with a
length of 12 feet, a width of 8.5 feet,
and a height of 4 feet. The container is
completely filled with contents that
weigh, on average, 0.25 pound per cubic
foot. What is the weight, in pounds, of the
contents in the container?

06 2015 07

1) 1,632
2) 408
3) 102
4) 92

15   A gallon of paint will cover
approximately 450 square feet. An
artist wants to paint all the outside
surfaces of a cube measuring 12 feet
on each edge. What is the *least* number
of gallons of paint he must buy to paint
the cube?

06 2015 19

1) 1
2) 2
3) 3
4) 4

16   The water tower in the picture below is
      modeled by the two-dimensional figure
      beside it. The water tower is composed of a
      hemisphere, a cylinder, and a cone. Let *C* be
      the center of the hemisphere and let *D* be the
      center of the base of the cone.

Source: http://en.wikipedia.org

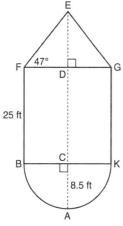

If $AC = 8.5$ feet, $BF = 25$ feet, and $m\angle EFD = 47°$,
determine and state, to the *nearest cubic foot*, the volume
of the water tower. The water tower was constructed to
hold a maximum of 400,000 pounds of water. If water
weighs 62.4 pounds per cubic foot, can the water tower be
filled to 85% of its volume and *not* exceed the weight
limit? Justify your answer.

The University of the State of New York
REGENTS HIGH SCHOOL EXAMINATION
GEOMETRY
Tuesday, June 19, 2018 — 9:15 a.m. to 12:15 p.m., only

Part I

Answer all 24 questions in this part. Each correct answer will receive 2 credits. No partial credit will be allowed. Utilize the information provided for each question to determine your answer. Note that diagrams are not necessarily drawn to scale. For each statement or question, choose the word or expression that, of those given, best completes the statement or answers the question. Record your answers on your separate answer sheet.

06 2018 01

1 After a counterclockwise rotation about point *X*, scalene triangle *ABC* maps onto $\triangle RST$, as shown in the diagram below.

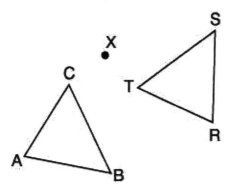

Which statement must be true?

1) $\angle A \cong \angle R$
2) $\angle A \cong \angle S$
3) $\overline{CB} \cong \overline{TR}$
4) $\overline{CA} \cong \overline{TS}$

2 In the diagram below, $\overline{AB} \parallel \overrightarrow{DEF}$, $\overline{AE}$
   and $\overline{BD}$ intersect at C, $m\angle B = 43°$,
   and $m\angle CEF = 152°$.

06 2018 02

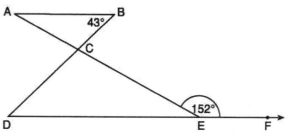

Which statement is true?
1) $m\angle D = 28°$
2) $m\angle A = 43°$
3) $m\angle ACD = 71°$
4) $m\angle BCE = 109°$

3 In the diagram below, line m is parallel
   to line n. Figure 2 is the image of Figure 1
   after a reflection over line m. Figure 3 is
   the image of Figure 2 after a reflection over
   line n.

06 2018 03

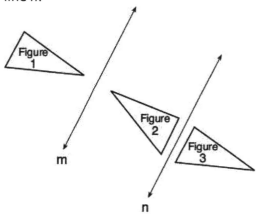

141

Which single transformation would carry Figure 1 onto
Figure 3?
1) a dilation
2) a rotation
3) a reflection
4) a translation

06 2018 04

4 In the diagram below, $\overline{AF}$, and $\overline{DB}$ intersect
at C, and $\overline{AD}$ and $\overline{FBE}$ are drawn such that
$m\angle D = 65°$, $m\angle CBE = 115°$, $DC = 7.2$,
$AC = 9.6$, and $FC = 21.6$.

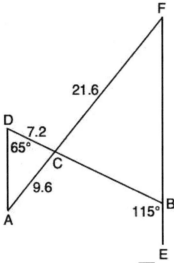

What is the length of $\overline{CB}$?
1) 3.2
2) 4.8
3) 16.2
4) 19.2

5   Given square *RSTV*, where $\overline{RS}$ = 9 cm.
    If square *RSTV* is dilated by a scale factor
    of 3 about a given center, what is the
    perimeter, in centimeters, of the image
    of *RSTV* after the dilation?

06 2018 05

    1) 12
    2) 27
    3) 36
    4) 108

6   In right triangle *ABC*, hypotenuse $\overline{AB}$ has
    a length of 26 cm, and side $\overline{BC}$ has a length
    of 17.6 cm. What is the measure of angle *B*,
    to the *nearest degree*?

06 2018 06

    1) 48°
    2) 47°
    3) 43°
    4) 34°

7   The greenhouse pictured below can be
    modeled as a rectangular prism with a half-
    cylinder on top. The rectangular prism is
    20 feet wide, 12 feet high, and 45 feet long.
    The half-cylinder has a diameter of 20 feet.

06 2018 07

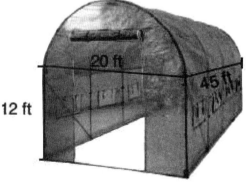

To the *nearest cubic foot*, what is the volume of the greenhouse?
1) 17,869
2) 24,937
3) 39,074
4) 67,349

8 In a right triangle, the acute angles have the relationship $\sin(2x + 4) = \cos(46)$.
What is the value of *x*?

06 2018 08

1) 20
2) 21
3) 24
4) 25

9 In the diagram below, $\overline{AB} \parallel \overline{DFC}$, $\overline{EDA} \parallel \overline{CBG}$, and $\overline{EFB}$ and $\overline{AG}$ are drawn.

06 2018 09

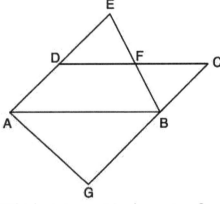

Which statement is always true?
1) $\triangle DEF \cong \triangle CBF$
2) $\triangle BAG \cong \triangle BAE$
3) $\triangle BAG \sim \triangle AEB$
4) $\triangle DEF \sim \triangle AEB$

10 The base of a pyramid is a rectangle with a width of 4.6 cm and a length of 9 cm. What is the height, in centimeters, of the pyramid if its volume is 82.8 cm³?

1) 6
2) 2
3) 9
4) 18

11 In the diagram below of right triangle AED, $\overline{BC} \parallel \overline{DE}$.

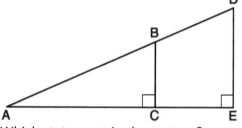

Which statement is always true?

1) $\dfrac{AC}{BC} = \dfrac{DE}{AE}$

2) $\dfrac{AB}{AD} = \dfrac{BC}{DE}$

3) $\dfrac{AC}{CE} = \dfrac{BC}{DE}$

4) $\dfrac{DE}{BC} = \dfrac{DB}{AB}$

12 What is an equation of the line that passes through the point $(6, 8)$ and is perpendicular to a line with equation $y = \frac{3}{2}x + 5$?

1) $y - 8 = \frac{3}{2}(x - 6)$

2) $y - 8 = -\frac{2}{3}(x - 6)$

3) $y + 8 = \frac{3}{2}(x + 6)$

4) $y + 8 = -\frac{2}{3}(x + 6)$

13 The diagram below shows parallelogram $ABCD$ with diagonals $\overline{AC}$ and $\overline{BD}$ intersecting at E.

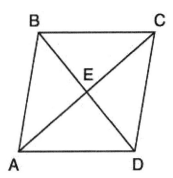

What additional information is sufficient to prove that parallelogram $ABCD$ is also a rhombus?

1) $\overline{BD}$ bisects $\overline{AC}$.

2) $\overline{AB}$ is parallel to $\overline{CD}$.

3) $\overline{AC}$ is congruent to $\overline{BD}$.

4) $\overline{AC}$ is perpendicular to $\overline{BD}$.

14 Directed line segment DE has endpoints $D(-4,-2)$ and $E(1,8)$. Point F divides $\overline{DE}$ such that $DF:FE$ is 2:3.

06 2018 14

What are the coordinates of F?

1) $(-3,0)$
2) $(-2,2)$
3) $(-1,4)$
4) $(2,4)$

15 Triangle DAN is graphed on the set of axes below. The vertices of $\triangle DAN$ have coordinates $D(-6,-1)$, $A(6,3)$, and $N(-3,10)$.

06 2018 15

What is the area of $\triangle DAN$?

1) 60
2) 120
3) $20\sqrt{13}$
4) $40\sqrt{13}$

147

16 Triangle *ABC*, with vertices at $A(0,0)$, $B(3,5)$, and $C(0,5)$, is graphed on the set of axes shown below.

06 2018 16

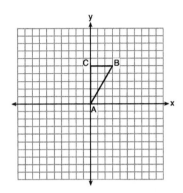

Which figure is formed when $\triangle ABC$ is rotated continuously about $\overline{BC}$?

1)

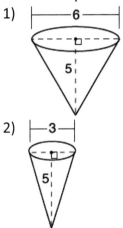

2)

3)

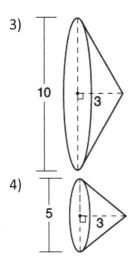

4)

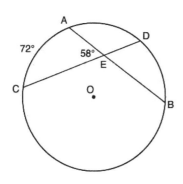

17 In the diagram below of circle O, chords $\overline{AB}$ and $\overline{CD}$ intersect at E.

06 2018 17

If $m\overset{\frown}{AC} = 72°$ and $m\angle AEC = 58°$, how many degrees are in $m\overset{\frown}{DB}$?

1) 108º
2) 65º
3) 44º
4) 14º

149

18 In triangle *SRK* below, medians $\overline{SC}$, $\overline{KE}$, and $\overline{RL}$ intersect at *M*.

06 2018 18

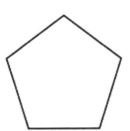

Which statement must always be true?
1) $3(MC) = SC$
2) $MC = \frac{1}{3}(SM)$
3) $RM = 2MC$
4) $SM = KM$

19 The regular polygon below is rotated about its center.

06 2018 19

Which angle of rotation will carry the figure onto itself?
1) 60°
2) 108°
3) 216°
4) 540°

20 What is an equation of circle O shown in the graph below?

06 2018 20

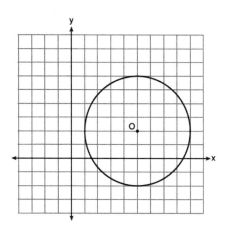

1) $x^2 + 10x + y^2 + 4y = -13$
2) $x^2 - 10x + y^2 - 4y = -13$
3) $x^2 + 10x + y^2 + 4y = -25$
4) $x^2 - 10x + y^2 - 4y = -25$

21 In the diagram below of $\triangle PQR$, $\overline{ST}$ is drawn parallel to $\overline{PR}$, $PS = 2$, $SQ = 5$, and $TR = 5$.

06 2018 21

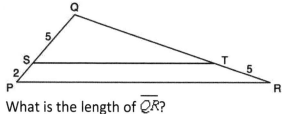

What is the length of $\overline{QR}$?

1) 7   2)   2

3) $12\frac{1}{2}$ 4) $17\frac{1}{2}$

151

22 The diagram below shows circle *O* with radii
$\overline{OA}$ and $\overline{OB}$. The measure of angle *AOB*
is 120°, and the length of a radius is 6 inches.

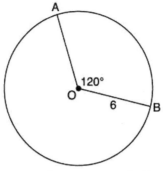

Which expression represents the length of arc *AB*, in
inches?

1) $\dfrac{120}{360}(6\pi)$

2) $120(6)$

3) $\dfrac{1}{3}(36\pi)$

4) $\dfrac{1}{3}(12\pi)$

23 Line segment *CD* is the altitude drawn to
hypotenuse $\overline{EF}$ in right triangle *ECF*. If
$EC = 10$ and $EF = 24$, then, to the *nearest*
tenth, *ED* is

1) 4.2
2) 5.4
3) 15.5
4) 21.8

24 Line *MN* is dilated by a scale factor of 2 centered at the point $(0, 6)$. If $\overleftrightarrow{MN}$ is represented by $y = -3x + 6$, which equation can represent $\overleftrightarrow{M'N'}$, the image of $\overleftrightarrow{MN}$?

06 2018 24

1) $y = -3x + 12$
2) $y = -3x + 6$
3) $y = -6x + 12$
4) $y = -6x + 6$

25 Triangle *A'B'C'* is the image of triangle *ABC* after a translation of 2 units to the right and 3 units up. Is triangle *ABC* congruent to triangle *A'B'C'*? Explain why.

06 2018 25

26 Triangle *ABC* and point $D(1, 2)$ are graphed on the set of axes below.

06 2018 26

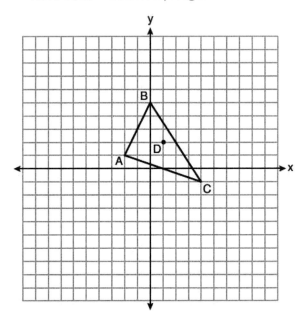

Graph and label $\triangle A'B'C'$, the image of $\triangle ABC$, after a dilation of scale factor 2 centered at point D.

27 Quadrilaterals *BIKE* and *GOLF* are graphed on the set of axes below.

06 2018 27

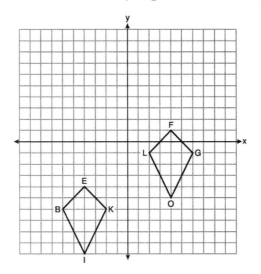

Describe a sequence of transformations that maps quadrilateral
BIKE onto quadrilateral *GOLF*.

28 In the diagram below, secants $\overline{RST}$ and $\overline{RQP}$, 06 2018 28
drawn from point *R*, intersect circle *O* at
S, *T*, *Q*, and *P*.

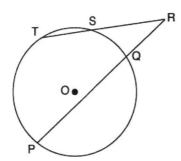

If $RS = 6$, $ST = 4$, and $RP = 15$, what is the length of $\overline{RQ}$?

29 Using a compass and straightedge, construct the median to side $\overline{AC}$ in △ABC below. [Leave all construction marks.]

06 2018 29

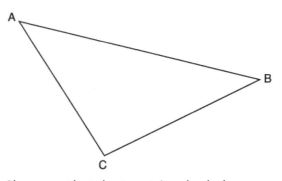

30 Skye says that the two triangles below are congruent. Margaret says that the two triangles are similar.

06 2018 30

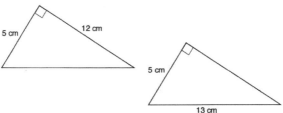

Are Skye and Margaret both correct? Explain why.

31 Randy's basketball is in the shape of a sphere with a maximum circumference of 29.5 inches. Determine and state the volume of the basketball, to the *nearest cubic inch*.

06 2018 31

32 Triangle *ABC* has vertices with coordinates $A(-1,-1)$, $B(4,0)$, and $C(0,4)$. Prove that $\triangle ABC$ is an isosceles triangle but *not* an equilateral triangle.
[The use of the set of axes below is optional.]

06 2018 32

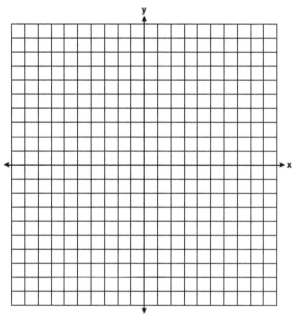

33 The map of a campground is shown below. 06 2018 33
Campsite *C*, first aid station *F*, and supply
station *S* lie along a straight path. The path
from the supply station to the tower, *T*, is
perpendicular to the path from the supply
station to the campsite. The length of path
$\overline{FS}$ is 400 feet. The angle formed by path
$\overline{TF}$ and path $\overline{FS}$ is 72°. The angle formed
by path $\overline{TC}$ and path $\overline{CS}$ is 55°.

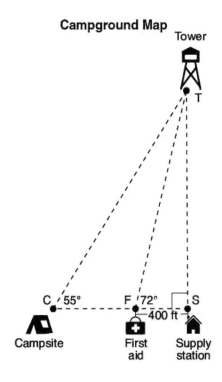

Campground Map

Determine and state, to the *nearest foot*, the distance
from the campsite to the tower.

34 Shae has recently begun kickboxing and
    purchased training equipment as modeled
    in the diagram below. The total weight of
    the bag, pole, and unfilled base is 270
    pounds. The cylindrical base is 18 inches
    tall with a diameter of 20 inches.
    The dry sand used to fill the base weighs
    95.46 lbs per cubic foot.

06 2018 34

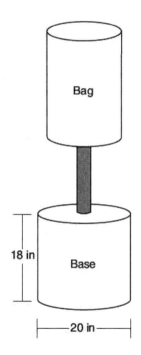

To the *nearest pound*, determine and state the total weight
of the training equipment if the base is filled to 85% of its
capacity.

35 Given: Parallelogram *ABCD*, $\overline{BF} \perp \overline{AFD}$, and $\overline{DE} \perp \overline{BEC}$

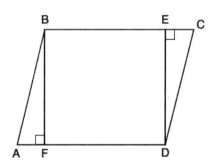

Prove: *BEDF* is a rectangle.

The University of the State of New York
REGENTS HIGH SCHOOL EXAMINATION
GEOMETRY
Friday, August 17, 2018 - 12:30 to 3:30 p.m., only

Part I

Answer all 24 questions in this part. Each correct answer will receive 2 credits. No partial credit will be allowed. Utilize the information provided for each question to determine your answer. Note that diagrams are not necessarily drawn to scale. For each statement or question, choose the word or expression that, of those given, best completes the statement or answers the question. Record your answers on your separate answer sheet. [48]

1   In the diagram below, $\overline{AEFB} \parallel \overline{CGD}$, and $\overline{GE}$ and $\overline{GF}$ are drawn.

08 2018 01

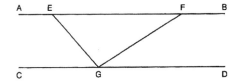

If $m\angle EFG = 32°$ and m $\angle$ AEG = 137°, what is the $m\angle EGF$?

(1) 11°   (3) 75°

(2) 43°   (4) 105°

2   If $\triangle ABC$ is mapped onto $\triangle DEF$ after a line reflection and $\triangle DEF$ is mapped onto $\triangle XYZ$ after a translation, the relationship between $\triangle ABC$ and $\triangle XYZ$ is that they are always

08 2018 02

(1) congruent and similar
(2) congruent but not similar
(3) similar but not congruent
(4) neither similar nor congruent

161

3 An isosceles right triangle whose legs
   measure 6 is continuously rotated
   about one of its legs to form a three-
   dimensional object.

   08 2018 03

   The three-dimensional object is a

   (1) cylinder with a diameter of 6
   (2) cylinder with a diameter of 12
   (3) cone with a diameter of 6
   (4) cone with a diameter of 12

4 In regular hexagon *ABCDEF* shown below,
   $\overline{AD}$, $\overline{BE}$, and $\overline{CF}$ all intersect at *G*.

   08 2018 04

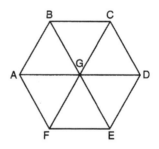

   When △*ABG* is reflected over $\overline{BG}$ and then
   rotated 180° about point *G*, △*ABG* is mapped onto

   (1) △*FEG*   (3) △*CBG*

   (2) △*AFG*   (4) △*DEG*

162

5 A right cylinder is cut perpendicular to its base. The shape of the cross section is a

08 2018 05

(1) circle
(2) cylinder
(3) rectangle
(4) triangular prism

6 Yolanda is making a springboard to use for gymnastics. She has 8-inch-tall springs and wants to form a 16.5° angle with the base, as modeled in the diagram below.

08 2018 06

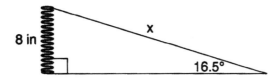

To the *nearest tenth of an inch,* what will be the length of the springboard, *x?*

(1) 2.3
(2) 8.3
(3) 27.0
(4) 28.2

7 In the diagram below of right triangle *ABC,* altitude $\overline{BD}$ is drawn to hypotenuse $\overline{AC}$.

08 2018 07

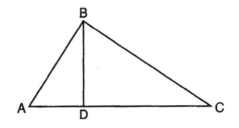

If *BD* = 4, *AD* = *x* − 6, and *CD* = *x*, what is the length of $\overline{CD}$?

(1) 5   (3) 8

(2) 2   (4) 11

8   Rhombus *STAR* has vertices S(-1,2), *T(2,3)*,
    A(3,0), and R(0, −l).

    What is the perimeter of rhombus *STAR?*

(1) $\sqrt{34}$ (3) $\sqrt{10}$

(2) $4\sqrt{34}$ (4) $4\sqrt{10}$

9   In the diagram below of △*HAR* and △*NTY,*
    angles *H* and *N* are right angles, and
    △*HAR* ~ △*NTY.*

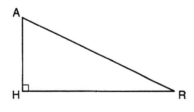
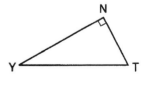

If *AR* = 13 and *HR* = 12, what is the measure of angle *Y*, to the *nearest degree?*

(1) 23°   (3) 65°

(2) 25°   (4) 67°

10 In the diagram below, $\overline{AKS}, \overline{NKC}, \overline{AN},$ and $\overline{SC}$ are drawn such that $\overline{AN} \cong \overline{SC}.$

08 2018 10

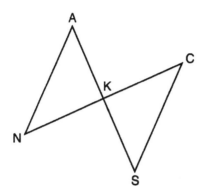

Which additional statement is sufficient to prove $\triangle KAN \cong \triangle KSC$ by AAS?

(1) $\overline{AS}$ and $\overline{NC}$ bisect each other.
(2) K is the midpoint of $\overline{NC}.$
(3) $\overline{AS} \perp \overline{CN}$
(4) $\overline{AN} \parallel \overline{SC}$

11 Which equation represents a line that is perpendicular to the line represented by $y = \frac{2}{3}x + 1$?

08 2018 11

(1) 3x + 2y = 12   (3) $y = \frac{3}{2}x + 2$

(2) 3x − 2y = 12   (4) $y = -\frac{2}{3}x + 4$

12 In the diagram of △ABC below, points D and
E are on sides $\overline{AB}$ and $\overline{CB}$ respectively, such
that $\overline{DE} \parallel \overline{AC}$.

08 2018 12

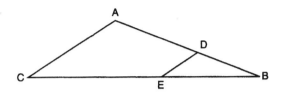

If EB is 3 more than DB, AB = 14, and CB = 21,
what is the length of $\overline{AD}$?

(1) 6   (3) 9

(2) 8   (4) 12

13 Quadrilateral MATH has both pairs of
opposite sides congruent and parallel.
Which statement about quadrilateral
MATH is always true?

08 2018 13

(1) $\overline{MT} \cong \overline{AH}$ (3) ∠MHT ≅ ∠ATH

(2) $\overline{MT} \perp \overline{AH}$ (4) ∠MAT ≅ ∠MHT

14 In the figure shown below, quadrilateral *TAEO* is circumscribed around circle *D*. The midpoint of $\overline{TA}$ is *R*, and $\overline{HO} \cong \overline{PE}$.

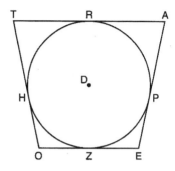

If *AP* = 10 and *EO* = 12, what is the perimeter of quadrilateral *TAEO*?

(1) 56

(3) 72

(2) 64

(4) 76

15 The coordinates of the endpoints of directed line segment *ABC* are *A* (−8,7) and *C* (7, −13). If *AB:BC* = 3:2, the coordinates of *B* are

(1) (1, −5)

(3) (−3,0)

(2) (−2, −1)

(4) (3, −6)

16 In triangle *ABC*, points *D* and *E* are on sides $\overline{AB}$ and $\overline{BC}$, respectively, such that $\overline{DE} \mid\mid \overline{AC}$, and *AD:DB* = 3:5.

08 2018 16

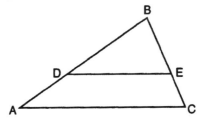

If *DB* = 6.3 and *AC* = 9.4, what is the length of $\overline{DE}$, to the *nearest tenth*?

(1) 3.8   (3) 5.9

(2) 5.6   (4) 15.7

17 In the diagram below, rectangle *ABCD* has vertices whose coordinates are *A*(7,1), *B*(9,3), *C*(3,9), and *D*(l,7).

08 2018 17

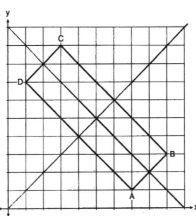

Which transformation will *not* can *y* the rectangle onto itself?

(1) a reflection over the line $y = x$
(2) a reflection over the line $y = -x + 10$
(3) a rotation of 180° about the point (6,6)
(4) a rotation of 180° about the point (5,5)

18 A circle with a diameter of 10 cm and a central angle of 30° is drawn below.

08 2018 18

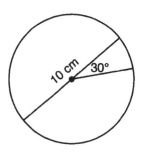

What is the area, to the *nearest tenth of a square centimeter,* of the sector formed by the 30° angle?

(1) 5.2   (3) 13.1

(2) 6.5   (4) 26.2

19 A child's tent can be modeled as a pyramid with a square base whose sides measure 60 inches and whose height measures 84 inches. What is the volume of the tent, to the *nearest cubic foot?*

(1) 35

(3) 82

(2) 58

(4) 175

20 In the accompanying diagram of right triangle ABC, altitude $\overline{BD}$ is drawn to hypotenuse $\overline{AC}$.

Which statement must always be true?

(1) $\frac{AD}{AB} = \frac{BC}{AC}$

(3) $\frac{BD}{BC} = \frac{AB}{AD}$

(2) $\frac{AD}{AB} = \frac{AB}{AC}$

(4) $\frac{AB}{BC} = \frac{BD}{AC}$

21 An equation of circle O is $x^2 + y^2 + 4x - 8y = -16$. The statement that best describes circle O is the

(1) center is (2, −4) and is tangent to the x-axis
(2) center is (2, −4) and is tangent to the y-axis
(3) center is (−2, 4) and is tangent to the x-axis
(4) center is (−2, 4) and is tangent to the y-axis

22 In $\triangle ABC$, $\overline{BD}$ is the perpendicular bisector of $\overline{ADC}$. Based upon this information, which statements below can be proven?

08 2018 22

    I. $\overline{BD}$ is a median.
    II. $\overline{BD}$ bisects $\angle ABC$.
    III. $\triangle ABC$ is isosceles.

(1) I and II, only   (3) II and III, only

(2) I and III, only   (4) I, II, and III

23 Triangle *RJM* has an area of 6 and a perimeter of 12. If the triangle is dilated by a scale factor of 3 centered at the origin, what are the area and perimeter of its image, triangle *R'J'M'* ?

08 2018 23

(1) area of 9 and perimeter of 15
(2) area of 18 and perimeter of 36
(3) area of 54 and perimeter of 36
(4) area of 54 and perimeter of 108

24 If $\sin (2x + 7)° = \cos (4x - 7)°$, what is the value of *x*?

08 2018 24

(1) 7   (3) 21

(2) 15   (4) 30

Part II

Answer all 7 questions in this part. Each correct answer will receive 2 credits.
Clearly indicate the necessary steps, including appropriate formula substitutions,
diagrams, graphs, charts, etc. Utilize the information provided for each question to
determine your answer. Note that diagrams are not necessarily drawn to scale.
For all questions in this part, a correct numerical answer with no work shown will
receive only I credit. All answers should be written in pen, except for graphs and
drawings, which should be done in pencil. [14]

25 In the circle below, $\overline{AB}$ is a chord. Using a
compass and straightedge, construct a
diameter of the circle.
[Leave all construction marks.]

08 2018 25

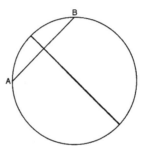

26 In parallelogram *ABCD* shown below, the
bisectors of ∠*ABC* and ∠*DCB* meet at *E*,
a point on $\overline{AD}$.

08 2018 26

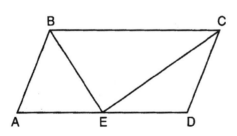

If m∠ *A* = 68°, determine and state *m*∠ *BEC.*

27 In circle A below, chord $\overline{BC}$ and diameter $\overline{DAE}$ intersect at F.

08 2018 27

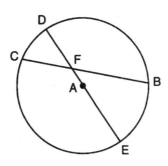

If $m\overset{\frown}{CD} = 46°$ and $m\overset{\frown}{DB} = 102°$, what is $m\angle CFE$?

28 Trapezoids $ABCD$ and $A''B''C''D''$ are graphed on the set of axes below.

08 2018 28

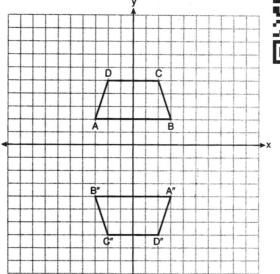

Describe a sequence of transformations that maps trapezoid $ABCD$ onto trapezoid $A''B''C''D''$.

29 In the model below, a support wire for a
telephone pole is attached to the pole and
anchored to a stake in the ground 15 feet
from the base of the telephone pole: Jamal
places a 6-foot wooden pole under the
support wire parallel to the telephone pole,
such that one end of the pole is on the ground
and the top of the pole is touching the support
wire. He measures the distance between the
bottom of the pole and the stake in the ground.

08 2018 29

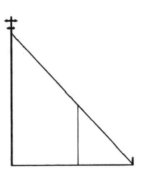

Jamal says he can approximate how high the support wire
attaches to the telephone pole by using similar triangles.

Explain why the triangles are similar.

30 Aliyah says that when the line $4x + 3y = 24$ is
dilated by a scale factor of 2 centered at the
point (3,4), the equation of the dilated line
is $y = -\frac{4}{3}x + 16$. Is Aliyah correct?
Explain why.
[The use of the set of axes below is optional.]

08 2018 30

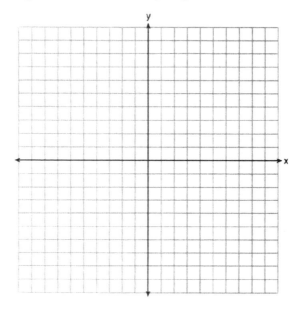

31 Ian needs to replace two concrete sections in his sidewalk, as modeled below. Each section is 36 inches by 36 inches and 4 inches deep. He can mix his own concrete for $3.25 per cubic foot.

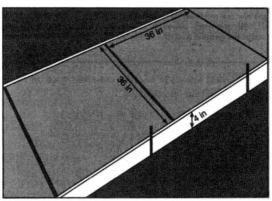

How much money will it cost Ian to replace the two concrete sections?

Part III
Answer all 3 questions in this part. Each correct answer will receive 4 credits. Clearly indicate the necessary steps, including appropriate formula substitutions, diagrams, graphs, charts, etc. Utilize the information provided for each question to determine your answer. Note that diagrams are not necessarily drawn to scale. For all questions in this part, a correct numerical answer with no work shown will receive only 1 credit. All answers should be written in pen, except for graphs and drawings, which should be done in pencil. [12]

32 Given: $\triangle ABC$, $\overline{AEC}$, $\overline{BDE}$ with
    $\angle ABE \cong \angle CBE$, and $LADE \cong \angle CDE$

08 2018 32

Prove: $\overline{BDE}$ is the perpendicular bisector of $\overline{AC}$.

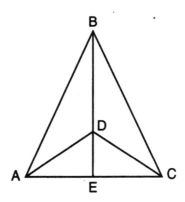

Fill in the missing statement and reasons below.

Statements	Reasons
(1) △ABC, $\overline{AEC}$, $\overline{BDE}$ with ∠ABE ≅ ∠CBE and ∠ADE ≅ ∠CDE	(1) Given
(2) $\overline{BD}$ ≅ $\overline{BD}$	(2) _____
(3) ∠BDA and ∠ADE are supplementary. ∠BDC and ∠CDE are supplementary.	(3) Linear pairs of angles are supplementary.
(4) _____	(4) Supplements of congruent angles are congruent.
(5) △ABD ≅ △CBD	(5) ASA
(6) $\overline{AD}$ ≅ $\overline{CD}$, $\overline{AB}$ ≅ $\overline{CB}$	(6) _____
(7) $\overline{BDE}$ is the perpendicular bisector of $\overline{AC}$.	(7) _____ _____ _____ _____

33 A homeowner is building three steps leading to a deck, as modeled by the diagram below. All three step rises, $\overline{HA}$, $\overline{FG}$, and $\overline{DE}$, are congruent, and all three step runs, $\overline{HG}$, $\overline{FE}$, and $\overline{DC}$, are congruent. Each step rise is perpendicular to the step run it joins. The measure of $\angle CAB = 36°$ and $m\angle CBA = 90°$.

08 2018 33

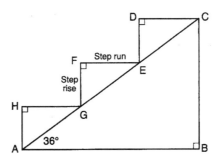

If each step run is parallel to $\overline{AB}$ and has a length of 10 inches, determine and state the length of each step rise, to the *nearest tenth of an inch.*

Determine and state the length of $\overline{AC}$, to the *nearest inch.*

34 A bakery sells hollow chocolate spheres. The larger diameter of each sphere is 4 cm. The thickness of the chocolate of each sphere is 0.5 cm. Determine and state, to the *nearest tenth of a cubic centimeter,* the amount of chocolate in each hollow sphere.

08 2018 34

The bakery packages 8 of them into a box. If the density of the chocolate is 1.308 g/cm^3, determine and state, to the *nearest gram,* the total mass of the chocolate in the box.

Part IV
Answer the question in this part. A correct answer will receive 6 credits. Clearly indicate the necessary steps, including appropriate formula substitutions, diagrams, graphs, charts, etc. Utilize the information provided for the question to determine your answer. Note that diagrams are not necessarily drawn to scale. For the question in this part, a correct numerical answer with no work shown will receive only I credit. All answers should be written in pen, except for graphs and drawings, which should be done in pencil. [6]

35 The vertices of quadrilateral *MATH* have coordinates *M*(−4,2), *A*(−1, −3), *T*(9,3), and *H*(6,8).

08 2018 35

Prove that quadrilateral *MATH* is a parallelogram.

[The use of the set of axes on the next page is optional.]

Prove that quadrilateral *MATH* is a rectangle.
[The use of the set of axes below is optional.]

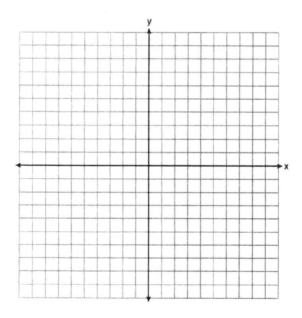

Accepted Solutions and Point Allocation

Angle and Segment Relationships

1. [2] 2
2. [2] 4
3. [2] 1
4. [2] 1
5. [4] A complete and correct explanation is written.

Angle and Segment Relationships in Triangles and Polygons

1. [4] 2402.2, and correct work is shown.
2. [2] 4
3. [2] 4
4. [2] 2
5. [2] 2
6. [2] 3
7. [2] 2
8. [2] 1
9. [2] 4
10. [2] 2
11. [2] 3
12. [4] All four reasons are correct.
13. [2] 3
14. [2] 2
15. [4] 0.49, and the correct work is shown. No, with a correct justification, is written.

Constructions

1. [2] A correct construction is drawn showing all appropriate arcs, and the hexagon is drawn.

2. [2] A correct construction is drawn showing all appropriate arcs.

3. [2] A correct construction is drawn showing all appropriate arcs, and the median to $\overline{AB}$ is drawn.

4. [4] A correct construction is drawn showing all appropriate arcs, A' and C' are correctly labeled, and a relationship is stated such as
$2 \cdot AC = A'C'$ or $AC = \frac{1}{2}A'C'$.

5. [2] A correct construction is drawn showing all appropriate arcs.

6. [4] A correct construction of $\triangle$ ABC $\cong \triangle$ XYZ is drawn showing all construction arcs. A correct theorem is stated to justify why the triangles are congruent.

7. [2] A correct construction is drawn showing all appropriate arcs.

8. [2] A correct construction is drawn showing all appropriate arcs.

Transformations

1. [2] 2.5, and appropriate work is shown.
2. [2] A correct sequence of transformations is written.
3. [2] 4
4. [2] 1
5. [2] 3
6. [2] 4
7. [4] Triangles *ABC* and *DEF* are graphed and labeled correctly, a reflection over the correct line is stated, and a correct explanation is written.
8. [2] $y = -\frac{3}{4}x + 5$ or an equivalent equation is written, and a correct explanation is written.
9. [2] A correct sequence of transformations is written.
10. [2] *When scoring these questions, all students should be awarded credit regardless of the answer, if any, they record on the answer sheet for this question.*
11. [2] *When scoring this question, either choice 1 or choice 3 should be awarded credit.*
12. [2] 1
13 [2] 3
14. [2] 2
15. [2] 2
16. [2] 1
17. [2] 4
18. [2] Triangle *A" B" C"* is graphed and labeled correctly.
19. [2] 60, and correct work is shown.
20. [2] 76, and a correct explanation is written.
21. [4] (7,1), and a correct explanation is written. Yes, and a correct explanation is written.
22. [2] 1
23. [2] 4
24. [2] 3

25. [2] A correct sequence of transformations is described.

26. [4] Dilation of $\frac{5}{2}$ centered at the origin is written. A correct explanation is written.

27. [2] 3

28. [2] 1

29. [2] 2

30. [2] 4

31. [2] Triangle $A'B'C'$ is graphed and labeled correctly.

32. [2] 4

33. [2] 1

34. [2] 2

35. [2] 1

36. [4] Point C, and a correct explanation is written. Yes, and a correct explanation is written.

37. [2] 4

38. [2] 4

39. [2] 1

40. [2] 2

41. [4] A complete and correct proof is written that includes a concluding statement, and a correct single rigid motion is stated.

42. [2] Yes, and a correct explanation is written.

43. [2] $y = 3x - 8$ or an equivalent equation is written, and correct work is shown.

44. [2] 1

45. [2] 1

46. [2] 4

47. [2] 1

48. [2] 1

Triangle Congruence

1. [4] A complete and correct proof that includes a conclusion is written.
2. [2] 2
3. [2] 3
4. [6] A complete and correct proof is written that includes both concluding statements.
5. [2] 3
6. [2] A correct explanation is written to explain why $\triangle ABC \cong \triangle XYZ$.
7. [4] Point C, and a correct explanation is written. Yes, and a correct explanation is written.
8. [2] 3
9. [2] A correct explanation is written.

Circles, Line and Segments on the Coordinate Plane

1. [2] 4
2. [2] 1
3. [2] 1
4. [2] 3
5. [2] 2
6. [2] 2
7. [2] 1
8. [2] 3
9. [2] 1
10. [2] 3
11. [2] 1
12. [2] 4
13. [2] 4
14. [2] Yes, and a correct justification is shown.
15. [2] 2
16. [2] 4

17. [2] 1
18. [2] 4
19. [2] 3
20. [2] 1
21. [2] (12, 2), and correct work is shown.
22. [2] 4
23. [2] 2
24. [2] (2, 5), and correct work is shown.
25. [2] 3
26. [2] 1
27. [2] (7,8), and correct work is shown.
28. [2] 3
29. [2] 1
30. [2] 2
31. [2] (–2, –3), and correct work is shown.

Circles

1. [4] A complete and correct proof that includes a concluding statement is written.
2. [2] Center (3,–4) and radius 9, and correct work is shown.
3. [2] 2
4. [2] 2
5. [2] 2.25π or an equivalent area in terms of pi is written, and appropriate work is shown.
6. [2] 2
7. [2] 4
8. [2] * *Due to a typographical error question #19 does not have a correct answer choice. All students receive credit for this question.*
9. [2] 1
10. [2] 21, and correct work is shown.
11. [6] A complete and correct proof that includes a concluding statement is written.
12. [2] 2

13. [2] 3
14. [2] Yes, and a correct explanation is written.
15. [2] 4
16. [2] 120 or an equivalent radian measure is found, and appropriate work is shown, such as a labeled diagram.
17. [2] 2
18. [2] 3
19. [2] 3
20. [2] 3
21. [2] 1
22. [2] 1
23. [2] 120 or $\frac{2\pi}{3}$, and correct work is shown.

Similarity

1. [2] 2
2. [2] 4
3. [2] 4
4. [2] 4
5. [2] 4
6. [2] A complete and correct explanation is written.
7. [2] *When scoring these questions, all students should be awarded credit regardless of the answer, if any, they record on the answer sheet for this question.*
8. [2] 4
9. [2] 2
10. [2] 3
11. [2] 3
12. [2] 4
13. [2] 3
14. [2] 1
15. [2] 2
16. [2] Correct work is shown, and a correct explanation is written.

17. [2] 1
18. [4] 42, and correct work is shown.
19. [2] 3
20. [2] 4
21. [2] 4
22. [2] 2
23. [2] 164, and correct work is shown.
24. [2] The triangles are similar, and a correct
    justification is stated.
25. [2] 3
26. [2] 3
27. [2] 4
28. [2] 6.6, and correct work is shown.
29. [4] 0.49, and correct work is shown. No, with a
    correct justification, is written.

Trigonometry

1. [2] 4
2. [2] 1
3. [2] 1
4. [6] 18,442 and 210, and correct work is shown.
5. [2] 4
6. [2] 1
7. [2] 3
8. [2] 1
9. [2] 15.5, and correct work is shown.
10. [4] 34.7, and correct work is shown.
11. [2] 4
12. [2] 4
13. [2] 17, and a correct explanation is written.
14. [2] 68, and appropriate work is shown.
15. [2] 4
16. [2] 3
17. [2] 3
18. [2] 32, and correct work is shown.

19. [6] 13.6, and correct work is shown.
20. [2] 1
21. [4] 582, and correct work is shown.
22. [2] 3
23. [2] 4
24. [2] 23, and correct work is shown.
25. [2] 6.6, and correct work is shown.

Parallelograms and Trapezoids

1. [6] A complete and correct proof that includes a
   concluding statement is written.
2. [2] 68, and correct work is shown.
3. [2] 3
4. [2] 4
5. [2] 2
6. [2] 4
7. [2] 3
8. [2] 1
9. [2] 1
10. [4] A complete and correct proof that includes a
    concluding statement is written.
11. [2] 3
12. [6] A complete and correct proof that includes
    concluding statements is written.
13. [2] 2
14. [2] 3
15. [2] A complete and correct proof that includes a
    concluding statement is written.
16. [6] A complete and correct proof that includes a
    conclusion is written.

17. [2] 4
18. [2] A correct explanation is written.
19. [4] A complete and correct proof is written that includes a concluding statement, and a correct single rigid motion is stated.

Coordinate Geometry Proofs

1. [4] Correct work is shown to prove that the midsegment is parallel to $\overline{PR}$ and is half the length of $\overline{PR}$, and concluding statements are written.

2. [2] $\overline{BC} \cong \overline{YZ}$ is indicated, and a correct explanation is written.

3. [6] A complete and correct proof that includes concluding statements that $PQRS$ is a rhombus and $PQRS$ is not a square is written.

4. [4] (7,1), and a correct explanation is written. Yes, and a correct explanation is written.

5. [2] 3

6. [2] 4

7. [4] 3 or 9.5, and correct work is shown.

8. [6] Correct work is shown to prove triangle RST is a right triangle. $P(0, 9)$ is stated, and correct work is shown to prove $RSTP$ is a rectangle.

Volume and Solids

1. [6] 8.5, 3752, 41, and correct work is shown.
2. [2] Yes, and a correct explanation is written.
3. [2] 3
4. [2] 2
5. [2] 0.6, and correct work is shown.
6. [2] A complete and correct explanation is written.
7. [2] 1
8. [2] 1

9. [2] 1
10. [2] 3
11. [2] 4
12. [2] 3
13. [2] 1
14. [6] 15, 24.9, and correct work is shown. A correct explanation is written.
15. [2] 1
16. [2] 2
17. [2] 3
18. [2] 2
19. [2] 4
20. [2] 4
21. [2] 4
22. [2] 2
23. [2] 2

Modeling

1. [2] 1
2. [4] 10.9, and correct work is shown.
3. [2] 3
4. [2] 2
5. [6] 44.53, and correct work is shown.
6. [2] 2
7. [4] 57.7, and correct work is shown.
8. [2] 2
9. [2] 1
10. [2] A, and correct work is shown.
11. [2] 1
12. [2] Ash is stated, and correct work is shown.
13. [6] 1885, $98.02, and $59.15, and correct work is shown.
14. [2] 3
15. [2] 2
16. [6] 7650 and No, and correct work is shown.

The University of the State of New York
REGENTS HIGH SCHOOL EXAMINATION
GEOMETRY
Tuesday, June 19, 2018 — 9:15 a.m. to 12:15 p.m., only
SCORING KEY AND RATING GUIDE

Part I

Allow a total of 48 credits, 2 credits for each of the following. Allow credit if the student has written the correct answer instead of the numeral 1, 2, 3, or 4.

(1) . . . . . 1 . . . . .   (2) . . . . . 3 . . . . .   (3) . . . . . 4 . . . . .

(4) . . . . . 3 . . . . .   (5) . . . . . 4 . . . . .   (6) . . . . . 2 . . . . .

(7) . . . . . 1 . . . . .   (8) . . . . . 1 . . . . .   (9) . . . . . 4 . . . . .

(10) . . . . . 1 . . . . .(11) . . . . 2 . . . . .   (12) . . . . 2 . . . . .

(13) . . . . . 4 . . . . .(14) . . . . 2 . . . . .   (15) . . . .1 . . . . .

(16) . . . . . 3 . . . . .(17) . . . . 3 . . . . .   (18). . . . 1 . . . . . .

(19) . . . . . 3 . . . . .(20) . . . . 2 . . . . .   (21) . . . . . 4 . . . . .

(22) . . . . . 4 . . . .   (23) . . . . 1 . . . . .   (24) . . . . . 2. . . . .

Part II

For each question, use the specific criteria to award a maximum of 2 credits. Unless otherwise specified, mathematically correct alternative solutions should be awarded appropriate credit.

(25) **[2]** Yes, and a correct explanation is written.

(26) **[2]** Triangle $A'B'C'$ is graphed and labeled correctly.

(27) **[2]** A correct sequence of transformations is described.

(28) **[2]** 4, and correct work is shown.

(29) **[2]** A correct construction is drawn showing all appropriate arcs, and the median to $\overline{AC}$ is drawn.

(30) **[2]** Yes, and a correct explanation is written.

(31) **[2]** 433 or 434, and correct work is shown.

Part III

For each question, use the specific criteria to award a maximum of 4 credits. Unless otherwise specified, mathematically correct alternative solutions should be awarded appropriate credit.

(32) **[4]** Correct work is shown to prove $\triangle ABC$ is an isosceles triangle and not an equilateral triangle, and correct concluding statements are made.

(33) **[4]** 1503, and correct work is shown.

(34) **[4]** 536, and correct work is shown.

Part IV

For this question, use the specific criteria to award a maximum of 6 credits. Unless otherwise specified, mathematically correct alternative solutions should be awarded appropriate credit.

(35) **[6]** A complete and correct proof that includes a concluding statement is written.

195

The University of the State of New York
REGENTS HIGH SCHOOL EXAMINATION
GEOMETRY

Friday, August 17, 2018 — 12:30 to 3:30 p.m., only

SCORING KEY AND RATING GUIDE

Part I

**Allow a total of 48 credits, 2 credits for each of the
following. Allow credit if the student has written the
correct answer instead of the numeral 1, 2, 3, or 4.**

(1) . . . . . 4 . . . . .   (2) . . . . . 1 . . . . .   (3) . . . . . 4 . . . . .

(4) . . . . . 1 . . . . .   (5) . . . . 3 . . . . .   (6) . . . . . 4 . . . . .

(7) . . . . 3 . . . . .   (8) . . . . . 4 . . . . .   (9) . . . . . 1 . . . . .

(10) . . . . . 4 . . . . . (11) . . . . . 1 . . . . . (12) . . . . . 2 . . . . .

(13) . . . . . 4 . . . . . (14) . . . . . 2 . . . . . (15) . . . . . 1 . . . . .

(16) . . . . 3 . . . . . (17) . . . . 3 . . . . . (18) . . . . 2 . . . . .

(19) . . . . 2 . . . . . (20) . . . . . 2 . . . . . (21) . . . . . 4 . . . . .

(22) . . . . . 4 . . . . . (23) . . . . 3 . . . . . (24) . . . . 2 . . . . .

Part II

For each question, use the specific criteria to award a maximum of 2 credits. Unless otherwise specified, mathematically correct alternative solutions should be awarded appropriate credit.

(25) **[2]** A correct construction is drawn showing all appropriate arcs.

(26) **[2]** 90, and correct work is shown, such as a labeled diagram.

(27) **[2]** 118, and correct work is shown.

(28) **[2]** A correct sequence of transformations is described.

(29) **[2]** A complete and correct explanation is written.

(30) **[2]** No is indicated, and a complete and correct explanation is written.

(31) **[2]** 19.50, and correct work is shown.

Part III

For each question, use the specific criteria to award a maximum of 4 credits. Unless otherwise specified, mathematically correct alternative solutions should be awarded appropriate credit.

(32) **[4]** Four statements or reasons are correct.

(33) **[4]** 7.3, 37, and correct work is shown.

(34) **[4]** 19.4 and 203, and correct work is shown.

Part IV

For this question, use the specific criteria to award a maximum of 6 credits. Unless otherwise specified, mathematically correct alternative solutions should be awarded appropriate credit.

(35) **[6]** A complete and correct proof that includes concluding statements that *MATH* is a parallelogram and *MATH* is a rectangle is written.

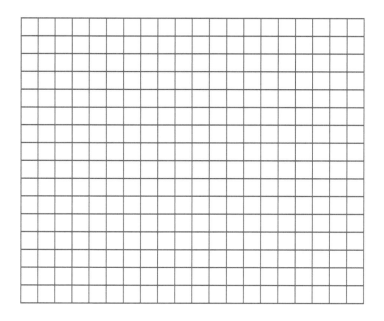

NOTES:

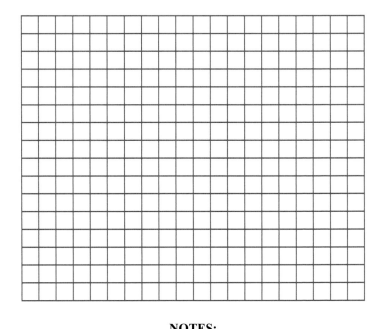

NOTES:

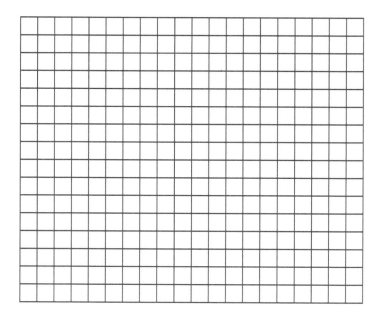

NOTES:

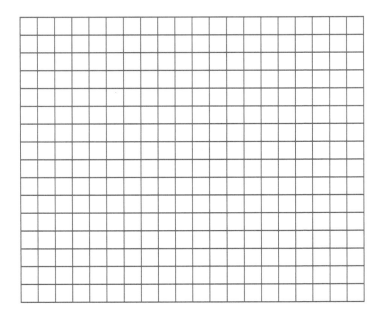

NOTES:

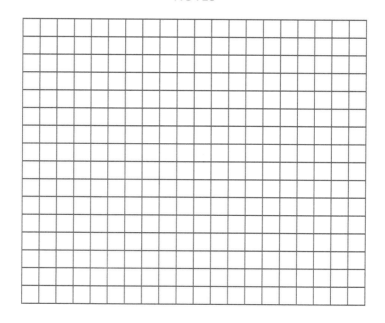

NOTES: